The "Teaching of English" Series

General Editor—DR. RICHARD WILSON

MORE NEW TALES FROM
SHAKESPEARE

No. 217

MORE NEW TALES FROM
❧ SHAKESPEARE ❧

Told by
G. B. HARRISON, D.LIT.

Illustrated by
C. WALTER HODGES

THOMAS NELSON AND SONS, LTD.
LONDON AND EDINBURGH

First published in this Series, 1940

CONTENTS

MORE NEW TALES FROM SHAKESPEARE

I

SIR JOHN FALSTAFF

WHEN King Richard II. was forced to abdicate the throne of England, he was succeeded by his cousin, Henry Bolingbroke, Duke of Lancaster, who became king as Henry IV. The new king soon found that kingship was a weary burden. The great nobles who had helped to put him on the throne began to turn against him and to plot rebellion, whilst nearer home his eldest son Henry, Prince of Wales, was a wild young man who spent most of his time indulging in madcap pranks with low companions. Of these the chief was Sir John Falstaff, an old knight of much experience who could be recognized anywhere, for he was enormously and incredibly fat. Falstaff was a rogue.

One morning Falstaff came to visit the Prince.

He was feeling melancholy, and in such a mood he wished that his reputation was better.

"I pray you, Hal," he moaned, "trouble me no more with vanity; I would that I knew where I could pick up a good reputation. The other day an old Lord of the Council rebuked me about you, sir; but I paid no attention. And yet he talked very wisely, but I did not regard him. You have done much harm to me, Hal; God forgive you for it. Before I knew you, Hal, I knew nothing; and now am I, if a man should speak truly, little better than one of the wicked. I must give over this life, and I will give it over."

Prince Hall let him talk on. Then he said, "Where shall we take a purse to-morrow, Jack?"

"Where you will, lad," cried Falstaff eagerly, "I'll make one; if I do not, call me villain."

"I see a good amendment of life in you," remarked the Prince, "from praying to purse taking."

"Why, Hal," said Falstaff innocently, "it is my vocation; it's no sin for a man to labour in his vocation."

At this Ned Poins, a fashionable young man, and another particular follower of the Prince, joined them.

"Good-morrow, Ned," said the Prince.

"Good-morrow, sweet Hal," he answered; and then to Falstaff, "What says Monsieur Remorse? What says Sir John Sack and Sugar?"

Then he told them that early the next morning there were pilgrims coming to Canterbury with rich offerings, and traders riding to London with fat purses.

"I have masks for you all," he said; "you have horses for yourselves. I have ordered supper to-morrow night at Eastcheap, so we may do it as safely as go to sleep. If you will go, I will stuff your purses full of crowns; if you will not, stay at home and be hanged."

Falstaff was all eagerness.

"Hal, will you make one?" he asked the Prince.

"Who, I rob? I a thief? Not I," Prince Hal replied.

Falstaff was disgusted.

"There's neither honesty, manhood, nor good-fellowship in you," he said.

"Well, then," replied the Prince, "for once I will be a madcap."

"Why, that's well said," Falstaff answered.

"Well, then," said the Prince, changing his mind, "I will stay at home."

"By the Lord," said Falstaff in disgust, "I will be a traitor when you are king."

"I don't care," replied the Prince.

"Sir John," said Poins, "leave the Prince and me alone. I will give him such good reasons for this adventure that he will go."

So Falstaff took himself off.

"Now, my good sweet honey lord," said Poins, "ride with us to-morrow. I have a jest that cannot be managed alone. Falstaff, Bardolph, Peto, and Gadshill shall rob those men that we have already waylaid; yourself and I shall not be there; and when they have the booty, if you and I do not rob them in turn, cut this head off from my shoulders."

"How shall we part company with them when we set out?" asked the Prince.

"Why," went on Poins, "we will go before—or after—them and appoint a place for meeting; and there we shall fail them. Then they will do the deed themselves; and no sooner done than we will set upon them."

"Yes," said the Prince, "but it is likely they will recognize us by our horses and our clothes."

"No, they will not see our horses; I will tie them in the wood. We will change our masks after we leave them, and I have linen overalls to cover our clothes."

"Yes," said the Prince, "but I think they will be too difficult for us."

"Well," replied Poins, "as for two of them, I know them to be as true-bred cowards as ever turned back; and for the third, if he fights longer than he sees reason, I'll give up wearing arms. The virtue of this jest will be the incomprehensible lies that this fat rogue will tell us when we meet at supper. How he fought with thirty at least;

what blows, what dangers he endured ; and the joke will be when we expose him."

The Prince agreed to go, and Poins went off to get everything ready.

The Prince was not quite what he seemed. His father, King Henry, Falstaff, Poins, and the others all supposed him to be merely a thoughtless, wild madcap. They did not know that there was a purpose in his pranks, for the Prince did not take his companions too seriously, and he knew that, when the time came, he would appear very differently.

The next morning, some hours before daylight, the carriers and travellers were stirring in their inn at Rochester. Gadshill pretended to help them. He was in league with the chamberlain of the inn, who told him of his guests, and where they were going, and what wealth they had about them.

" There's a franklin," said he, " from the Weald of Kent has brought three hundred marks * with him in gold ; I heard him tell it to one of his companions last night at supper, and *he* has much wealth with him too."

So Gadshill thanked him, and went out to join the others in the darkness.

Prince Henry and Poins by this time were at the meeting-place. They had come on after Falstaff and the others, and there they had

* A mark was worth 13s. 4d.

found Falstaff's horse, which Poins had taken and hidden. Falstaff stumped up and down in anger.

"Poins! Hal!" he cried.

"Peace," whispered the Prince, coming out of the darkness behind him, "what a brawling you keep up!"

"Where's Poins, Hal?"

"He has walked up to the top of the hill; I will go and look for him."

"I am accursed to rob in that thief's company," muttered Falstaff to himself; "the rascal has removed my horse and tied him I know not where. Well, if I escape hanging for killing the rogue, I will die a clean death for all this. I have sworn to leave his company hourly for the last twenty-two years, and yet I am bewitched by him. It can be nothing but witchcraft. Poins! Hal!" he cried out, "Bardolph! Peto!"

He was soon puffed with walking up and down the hill.

"I'll starve," he grumbled, "if I rob a foot farther."

There was a whistle in the darkness. Falstaff answered it, and he called out again, "Give me my horse, you rogues! Give me my horse, and be hanged!"

"Peace!" said the Prince, again coming up to Falstaff. "Lie down and listen if you can hear the tramp of travellers."

"Have you any levers to lift me up again when I am down?" asked Falstaff.

Gadshill, Bardolph, and Peto approached.

"Stand!" cried Bardolph.

"So I do, against my will," said Falstaff. Poins recognized the voice, and asked Bardolph for his news.

"Put on your masks," he cried. "There's money of the King's coming down the hill; it is going to the King's Exchequer."

"You lie, you rogue, it's going to the King's Tavern," Falstaff replied.

"Sirs," commanded the Prince, "you four shall confront them in the narrow lane. Ned Poins and I will walk lower. If they escape from your encounter, then they meet us."

"How many are there of them?" asked Peto.

"Some eight or ten," Gadshill replied.

"Will they not rob us?" asked Falstaff a little anxiously.

"What? A coward, Sir John Paunch?" said the Prince.

"Indeed, I am not John of Gaunt, your grandfather; but yet no coward, Hal."

"Well, we leave that to the proof," replied the Prince.

"Jack," whispered Poins, "your horse stands behind the hedge; when you need him you will find him there. Good-bye, and stand fast."

The Prince and Poins went farther down the

hill and there put on their disguise. The travellers approached. Suddenly Falstaff and the rest sprang out upon them. They seized their arms and bound them, and then took the purses from their pockets. Then the four went some way from the road, and there sat down to count the booty.

"Come, my masters," said Falstaff, "let us share, and then to horse before daylight. If the Prince and Poins are not two arrant cowards, there's no right anywhere. There's no more valour in that Poins than in a wild duck."

So they counted the money on the ground, and were about to divide it into four portions when suddenly with a yell the Prince and Poins set upon them. Bardolph, Peto, and Gadshill took to their heels at once and ran. Falstaff drew his sword and exchanged a blow or two with Poins, but when he saw that there were two to one, and both nimble young men, he too took to his heels and fled, roaring for mercy. The Prince and Poins gathered up the money, mounted their horses, and rode off merrily to London.

That evening both went down to the Boar's Head Tavern to wait for Falstaff. After a while the four would-be robbers came into the tavern. Falstaff was bold and indignant; the others looked sheepish.

"Welcome, Jack!" cried Poins. "Where have you been?"

Falstaff looked at the pair of them scornfully and called for a drink.

"A plague on all cowards, I say, and vengeance too, Amen! Give me a cup of sack, boy. Rather than lead this life I will make stockings and darn them. A plague on all cowards! Give me a cup of sack, you rogue. Is there no valour left?" he said.

"Did you ever see the sun melt a dish of butter?" said the Prince to Poins, pointing to Falstaff, who was hot and gleaming with sweat. "If you did, look at that."

Falstaff put down the cup and wiped his lips. "Go your way, old Jack," he said sorrowfully to himself; "die when you will. There live not three good men unhanged in England; and one of them is fat and grows old; a plague on all cowards, I say again!"

"What's that, wool-sack?" asked the Prince. "What are you muttering?"

"If I do not beat you out of your kingdom with a wooden sword, and drive all your subjects before you like a flock of wild geese, I'll never wear hair on my face any more. You Prince of Wales!" muttered Falstaff.

"Why, you round man," said the Prince, "what's the matter?"

"Are you not a coward?" said Falstaff. "Answer me that. Yes, and Poins there?"

Poins came at him fiercely, "You fat paunch! if you call me coward, by the Lord I'll stab you."

" I call you coward ? " said Falstaff mildly. " I'll see you damned before I call you a coward ; but I would give a thousand pounds that I could run as fast as you can. You are straight enough in the shoulders ; you do not care who sees your back. Do you call that backing of your friends ? A plague upon such backing ! Give me them that will look me in the face. Give me a cup of sack. I am a rogue if I have drunk to-day."

" Oh, you villain ! " gasped the Prince, " your lips are scarcely dry since you last drank."

" All's one for that." He drank another cup and again muttered, " A plague on all cowards."

" What's the matter ? " the Prince asked.

" What's the matter ? " echoed Falstaff. " Four of us here have taken a thousand pounds this morning."

" Where is it Where is it ? " said the Prince.

" Where is it ? Taken from us it is : a hundred upon poor four of us."

" What, a hundred men ? " asked the Prince.

" I am a rogue if I did not fight with a dozen of them for two hours on end," Falstaff replied. " I escaped by a miracle. I am eight times thrust through the doublet ; four through the hose ; my buckler cut through and through ; my sword cut like a hand-saw ; I never fought better since I was a man. All would not do ; a plague on all cowards ! " He pointed at the others, " Let them speak : if they speak more or less than the truth, they are villains and the sons of darkness ! "

" Speak, sirs," said the Prince to the other three worthies. " How was it ? "

" We four set upon some dozen——" began Gadshill.

" Sixteen at least, my lord," put in Falstaff.

" And bound them," said Gadshill.

" No, no," said Peto, " they were not bound."

" You rogue ! " broke in Falstaff, " they were bound, every man of them, or else I am a Jew."

Gadshill went on, " As we were sharing, some six or seven fresh men set upon us——"

" And unbound the rest, and then the others came in," said Falstaff.

" What ? Did you fight with them all ? " asked the Prince.

" All ! " replied Falstaff, " I don't know what you call all ; but if I did not fight with fifty of them, I am a bunch of radish. If there were not two or three and fifty upon poor old Jack, then I am no two-legged creature."

" I pray God you have not murdered some of them," said the Prince.

" No, that's past praying for ; I have peppered two of them ; two I am sure I have paid ; two rogues in linen overalls. I tell you, Hal, if I lie, spit in my face."

Falstaff was now warming up to his tale ; with

his sword in his right hand, and buckler in his left, he demonstrated his heroism.

"Here I lay and I bore my point thus. Then four rogues in linen overalls went for me——"

"What, four? You said two a minute ago," said the Prince.

"Four, Hal; I told you four," said Falstaff.

"Yes, yes, he said four," said Poins, nudging the Prince.

"These four," Falstaff went on, "came all in front of me and thrust at me with might and main. I made no more ado, but took all their seven points in my target. Thus."

"Seven?" asked the Prince. "Why, there were but four just now."

"In linen," said Falstaff.

"Yes," said Poins, "in linen overalls."

"Seven," declared Falstaff, "or by my sword I am a villain."

"Let him alone," whispered the Prince to Poins, "we shall have more soon."

"Do you hear me, Hal?" went on Falstaff.

"Yes, and mark you too, Jack."

"Do so, for it's worth listening to. These nine in linen that I told you of——"

"So? Two more already," murmured the Prince.

"Their points being broken, began to give me ground. I followed close. Came in hand and foot; and seven of the eleven I pierced."

"Oh, monstrous!" said the Prince, "eleven linen men grown out of two!"

"But, as the devil would have it," went on Falstaff, "three knaves in Kendal green came behind me and thrust at me. It was so dark, Hal, that you could not see your hand."

The Prince had heard enough.

"These lies are like their father that begets them," he answered, "gross as a mountain, open, palpable. Why, you clay-brained fool, you obscene lump of candle grease——"

"What, are you mad? Are you mad? Is not the truth the truth?" cried Falstaff, taken aback for the moment.

"Why," said the Prince, "how could you know these men in Kendal green when it was so dark you could not see your hand? Come, your reason; what is your reason?"

Falstaff stood on his dignity.

"What," said he, "upon compulsion? If I were tortured by all the racks in the world I would not tell you on compulsion. Give you a reason on compulsion! If reasons were as plentiful as blackberries I would not give you a reason on compulsion; not I!"

The Prince rose and came towards him.

"This sanguine coward," he cried, "this bed-presser, this horseback-breaker, this huge hill of flesh——"

"You starveling! you elf-skin, you dried ox

tongue, you stock fish ! " retorted Falstaff. " Oh
for breath to say what you are like ! you tailor's
yard, you sheath, you bow-case, you——"

" Well," replied the Prince, " breathe awhile,
and then begin again ; and when you have tired
yourself out, hear me speak this."

" Mark, Jack," said Poins.

The Prince looked Falstaff straight in the face.

" We two saw you four set on four, bind them,
and take their wealth. Mark now, how a plain
tale shall put you down. Then we two set on
you four ; in a word, frightened you off from the
prize ; and we have it, yes, and can show it you
here in the house ; and, Falstaff, you carried
yourself away as nimbly, and as quickly, and
roared for mercy, and went on running and
roaring like a bull calf. What a rogue you are to
hack your sword as you have done, and then to
say it was in fight ! What trick, what device,
can you now find to cover you from this open
shame ? "

" Come, let's hear, Jack, what trick have you
now ? " said Poins.

Falstaff was not in the least put out. He
looked from one to the other. Then he said quite
calmly : " By the Lord, I knew you as well as he
that made you. Was it for me to kill the heir-
apparent ? Should I turn upon the true Prince ?
Why, you know I am as valiant as Hercules. But
beware instinct. The lion will not touch the true

prince. I shall think the better of myself and you during my life ; I for a valiant lion and you for a true prince. But, by the Lord, I'm glad you have the money."

Then he cried out to the hostess of the inn to shut the doors. " Gallants ! lads ! boys ! hearts of gold ! Shall we be merry ? Shall we have a play extempore ? "

" The plot shall be your running away," said the Prince.

" Ah, no more of that, Hal, if you love me," Falstaff replied.

The hostess came in in great alarm.

" Oh, my lord the Prince ! " she cried.

" How now, my Lady the Hostess ! What is it ? "

" My lord, there is a nobleman of the Court at the door who would speak with you : he says he comes from your father."

" What kind of man is he," asked Falstaff.

" An old man."

" What does Gravity out of his bed at midnight ? Shall I give him his answer ? "

" Yes, do, Jack," said the Prince.

" I'll send him packing," Falstaff answered, as he lumbered out of the room.

The Prince looked at Bardolph, Peto, and Gadshill, who stood sheepishly before him.

They were not a handsome trio ; Bardolph especially, for his face and his nose were fiery red and covered with spots and pimples.

" Now, sirs," said Prince Hal, " you fought bravely. You are lions too. You ran away upon instinct ; you will not touch the true Prince, oh no ! "

" I ran when I saw the others run," muttered Bardolph.

" Now tell me truly," the Prince asked, " how did Falstaff's sword come to be so hacked ? "

" Why," Peto answered, " he hacked it with his dagger, and said he would swear truth out of England and make you believe it was done in fight ; and he persuaded us to do the same."

" Yes," said Bardolph, " and to tickle our noses with spear-grass to make them bleed, and then to daub our garments with it, and swear it was the blood of true men. I blushed to hear his wicked devices."

The Prince looked at Bardolph's red face.

" Oh, you villain. You stole a cup of sack eighteen years ago, and ever since then you have blushed naturally. You had fire and sword on your side, and yet you ran away."

Falstaff came back.

" Here comes lean Jack," cried the Prince. " Here comes bare-bone. How long is it, Jack, since you saw your own knee ? "

" My own knee ! " said Falstaff. " When I was about your years, Hal, I was no larger than an eagle's talon in the waist ; I could have crept into any alderman's thumb-ring. A plague of sighing and grief! It blows a man up like a bladder. There's wicked news abroad. That was Sir John Bracy from your father. You must go to the Court in the morning. That same mad fellow of the north, Hotspur, and that wild man of Wales — what do you call him ? — Owen Glendower, and his son-in-law Mortimer, and old Northumberland, and that sprightly Scot of Scots, Douglas, are all out against your father. Tell me, Hal, are you not horribly afraid ? You being heir-apparent."

" Not a whit," answered the Prince. " I lack some of your instinct."

" Well," said Falstaff, " you will be horribly chidden to-morrow when you come to your father. If you love me, rehearse your answer."

" You be my father then, and examine me upon the particulars of my life," said Hal.

" Shall I ? " said Falstaff gleefully. He looked round.

" This chair shall be my throne ; this dagger my sceptre ; and this cushion my crown."

So he sat down with the cushion on his head, and his dagger in his right hand. He called for a cup of sack to make his eyes look red as if he had been weeping. Then he assumed the air of a tragedy king.

The Prince went up to him and bowed, " Well, here is my leg," said he, and knelt before him.

" And this is my speech," replied Falstaff.
" Stand aside nobility."

The hostess was almost weeping with laughter.

" Peace, good pint pot," said Falstaff, " peace,
good tickle-brain."

Then he cleared his throat and spoke to the
Prince very pompously :

" Harry, I do not only marvel where you spend
your time, but also how you are accompanied ;
for though the camomile, the more it is trodden
on the faster it grows, yet youth the more it is
wasted the sooner it wears. That you are my
son I have partly your mother's word, partly my
own opinion, but chiefly a villainous trick of your
eye, and a foolish hanging of your lower lip. If
then you are a son to me, here lies the point :
why, being my son, are you so pointed at ? Shall
the son of England prove a thief and take purses ?
There is a question to be asked. There is a thing,
Harry, which you have often heard of, and it is
known to many in our land by the name of pitch ;
this pitch, as ancient writers do report, does defile ;
so does the company you keep. For, Harry, now
I do not speak to you in drink, but in tears ; not
in pleasure, but in passion ; not in words only,
but in woes also. And yet there is a virtuous man
whom I have often noted in your company, but I
do not know his name."

" What manner of man ? " asked the Prince as
if surprised.

"A goodly, portly man, a corpulent man, of a cheerful look, a pleasing eye, and a most noble appearance. I think his age is some fifty or, perhaps, sixty years; and now I remember it, his name is Falstaff. I see virtue in his looks. If then the tree may be known by the fruit, as the fruit by the tree, then there is virtue in Falstaff. Keep in with him; banish the rest. And now tell me, you naughty varlet, tell me, where have you been this month?"

The Prince jumped up.

"You speak like a king? You take my place, and I will play my father."

"Depose me?" said Falstaff. "If you do it half so gravely or so majestically, both in word and matter, hang me up by the heels for a rabbit-sucker."

The Prince and Falstaff changed places, the Prince imitating his father, and Falstaff pretending to be the young Prince.

"Now, Harry, where have you come from?"

"My noble lord, from Eastcheap," said Falstaff.

"The complaints I hear of you are grievous."

"My lord, they are false," protested Falstaff; and then to the spectators, "I'll show you how to act a young Prince."

"Do you swear that?" said the Prince. "In future never come near me. You are violently carried away from grace. There is a devil haunts you in the likeness of a fat old man ; a barrel of a man is your companion. Why do you converse with that trunk of humours, that swollen parcel of dropsies, that huge bombard of sack, that stuffed bag, that reverend vice, that grey iniquity, that father ruffian, that vanity in years ? Wherein is he good, but to taste sack and drink it ? Wherein neat and clean, but to carve a chicken and eat it ? Wherein cunning, but in craft ? Wherein crafty, but in villany ? Wherein villainous, but in all things ? Wherein worthy, but in nothing ? "

" Your Grace," said Falstaff innocently, " whom do you mean ? "

" That villainous, abominable misleader of youth, Falstaff, that old white-bearded Satan."

" My lord, I know the man," said Falstaff.

" I know you do."

" But to say I know more harm in him than in myself, were to say more than I know. That he is old, the more the pity ; his white hairs do witness it. If sack and sugar be a fault, God help the wicked ! If to be old and merry be a sin, then many an old host that I know is damned. If to be fat is to be hated, then Pharaoh's lean kine are to be loved."

Then, growing more eloquent, he went on, " No, my good lord. Banish Peto, banish Bardolph, banish Poins ; but for sweet Jack Falstaff, kind Jack Falstaff, true Jack Falstaff, valiant Jack

Falstaff, and therefore more valiant, being, as he is, old Jack Falstaff, banish him not from your Harry's company ; banish plump Jack, and banish all the world."

" I do, I will," cried the Prince.

There was a great knocking at the street door. The hostess and Bardolph went out to see what was happening. Bardolph ran back terrified, for the sheriff and the watch were in the street, and Bardolph feared the worst.

" Get out, you rogue," cried Falstaff. " Finish the play ; I have still much to say on behalf of Falstaff."

The hostess came in wringing her hands.

" Oh, my lord ! my lord ! " she cried.

" What's the matter ? " said the Prince impatiently.

" The sheriff and all the watch are at the door ; they have come to search the house. Shall I let them in ? " she asked.

The Prince told Falstaff to hide behind the curtain and the rest to go upstairs. When they were all hidden, he gave orders that the sheriff should be admitted.

When the sheriff entered, he asked him what he wanted.

" Forgive me, my lord," he answered, " but a hue and cry has followed certain men into this house."

" What men ? " asked the Prince.

" One of them is well known, my lord," said the sheriff, " a gross fat man."

" The man, I do assure you, is not here," the Prince replied, " for I myself have employed him ; and, sheriff, I promise you that, by to-morrow dinner-time, I will send him to answer you or any man with anything he shall be charged with. So let me entreat you to leave the house."

" I will, my lord. There are two gentlemen who have been robbed of three hundred marks."

" It may be so," said the Prince, " and if he has robbed these men, he shall answer for it. Good-night."

" Good-night, my noble lord," answered the sheriff.

" I think it is good-morning, is it not ? " said the Prince.

" Indeed, my lord, I think it is two o'clock."

When the sheriff had gone, the Prince said to Peto : " This oily rascal is known as well as St. Paul's Church. Call him out."

Peto went to the curtain and lifted it. There was Falstaff with his hands clasped across his stomach fast asleep, and snoring.

" Search his pockets," said the Prince. Peto went through his pockets and could find nothing but a bill or two.

" Let him sleep till daylight," said the Prince. " I will go to the Court in the morning. We must all go to the wars. I will get this fat rogue a commission. He will die if he has to walk a mile. As for the money, that shall be paid back with interest. Good-morning, Peto."

"Good-morning, my good lord," replied Peto, as the Prince left him.

So Falstaff went to the wars. The Prince obtained for him a commission as captain of a company of infantry, and, with Bardolph as his lieutenant, Falstaff went round to collect his company. He did well for himself. He would call up householders for service, rich farmers' sons or bachelors about to be married; any man who would be unwilling to serve as a soldier and ready to pay to get out of it. By this means he made over £300 in a few days. When at last his company was complete it consisted of old soldiers, ragged serving men, tapsters and ostlers out of work. No one had ever seen such scarecrows. As he marched along at their head a man called out and told him that he had unloaded all the gibbets and pressed the dead bodies. Most of them came out of prison, and in all the company there was only one complete shirt. Falstaff was ashamed of his rascals. But when the Prince saw them and spoke to him about them, he was quite ready to justify himself. "Good enough to toss," said he, "food for powder; food for powder; they'll fill a pit as well as better." With this ragged regiment at his heels at last he reached

Shrewsbury, where the army of the rebels was
waiting for the King.

Falstaff had no great liking for battles. He was
not a man greatly stirred by honour. " Honour,"
said he, " cannot set a leg or an arm, or take away
the pain of a wound. Honour ? Honour is the
mere word ; air." Honour was no good to the
dead, and even among the living it could not live
for jealousy.

So the battle began, and Falstaff looked to see
where he could best benefit himself. He led his
ragamuffins up and down, and most of them were
shot. Falstaff did not care, for he would draw
their pay.

By and by he came upon Prince Hal and
Hotspur. They had long sought each other in the
battle. Now they met, and were fighting to the
death, each eager to win the honour of victory.
Falstaff looked on with admiration, shouting
encouragement to the Prince. But then there
rushed towards him a ferocious enemy. It was
Douglas the Scot. Falstaff had less zeal for
honour than either the Prince or Hotspur, and
after a few blows had been struck he rolled on the
ground as if he were dead. Douglas made off to
seek new enemies. At last Hotspur fell, mortally
wounded. The Prince grieved for a while over his
great enemy. Then he gently covered his face
with his scarf. Near by he saw Falstaff, seemingly
lying dead on the ground. He looked down at

the huge body of his old friend. Then he went off to join his father.

Falstaff lay quite still until he was alone. He opened an eye. Then he sat up and mopped his face. He was very pleased with himself for having escaped so cunningly from the Douglas.

" The better part of valour," said he sagely to himself, " is discretion ; in which better part I have saved my own life."

Then he struggled to his feet and went over to the place where Percy's body lay. He was a little frightened at first of Percy's body ; for supposing Percy too was pretending to be dead, what then ? To make sure of that, he wounded the corpse with his sword. Then taking it by the heels he hoisted it on his back and struggled forward with it. Meanwhile the Prince had found his brother, John of Lancaster, and was bringing him to see the dead Percy and Falstaff. To his great wonder he saw Falstaff very much alive. Falstaff tumbled the body of Hotspur down to the ground. " There is Percy," said he triumphantly. " If your father will do me any honour, so ; if not, let him kill the next Percy himself. I look to be made either Earl or Duke, I can assure you."

" Why," said the Prince, " I killed Percy myself and saw you dead."

" Did you ? " said Falstaff pityingly. " Lord, Lord, how this world is given to lying. I grant you I was down, and out of breath. And so was he. But we rose together in one instant, and fought a whole hour by Shrewsbury clock. If I may be believed, so ; if not, let them that should reward valour bear the sin upon their own heads. I swear by my life I gave him this wound in the thigh ; if the man were alive and would deny it, I would make him eat a piece of my sword."

The Prince laughed at Falstaff's lies, and told him to hoist his luggage on his back and he would see about rewarding him.

So Hotspur and friends were beaten, and the King and his soldiers returned to London ; but the rebellion was not at an end, for Hotspur's father, the old Earl of Northumberland, and others of his party were gathering fresh forces in the north.

When Sir John came back to London, the Prince sent him a page, who followed him here and there carrying his sword and buckler, and looking like a little sucking pig behind a huge old sow. There were still troubles for Falstaff. The robbery affair had not been forgotten, so that when Falstaff met the Lord Chief Justice walking in one of the streets of London, he tried to avoid him. But the Lord Chief Justice recognized Falstaff and sent his man to tell him to come to speak to him. Falstaff pretended not to hear. The man plucked him by the arm. Falstaff looked surprised.

" What ? " said he severely. " A young man begging ? Are there no wars ? Is there no employment ? Does the King lack subjects ? Do not the rebels need soldiers ? Though it is a shame not to be on the side of the King, it is better to be a rebel than a beggar."

" You mistake me, sir," replied the man, confused by Falstaff's flow of words.

" What ? Did I say you were an honest man ? If I did, I lied," said Falstaff.

" Sir," at last the servant said, " my lord would speak with you."

The Lord Chief Justice, seeing Falstaff's reluctance, himself came over to speak to him.

Falstaff greeted him very affably.

" My good lord," he said, taking off his cap and bowing, " I am glad to see your lordship abroad ; I heard your lordship was sick ; I hope your lordship goes abroad advisedly. Your lordship, I humbly beseech you to have good care of your health."

" Sir John," replied the Lord Chief Justice sternly, " I sent for you before your expedition to Shrewsbury."

Falstaff pretended not to have heard this remark.

" If it please your lordship, I hear his Majesty has returned from Wales somewhat unwell."

" I do not talk of his Majesty," said the Lord

Chief Justice. " You would not come when I sent for you ? "

" And I hear, moreover," went on Falstaff, " that his Majesty is suffering from this apoplexy."

" Well, God mend him," said the Lord Chief Justice. " I pray you let me speak with you."

" This apoplexy, as I take it," Falstaff continued, " is a kind of lethargy, a kind of tingling."

" Why do you talk to me of that ? "

" It arises from much grief, and study, and perturbation of the brain ; I have read the cause of its effects ; it is a kind of deafness."

" I think you have fallen into the disease," said the Lord Chief Justice, " for you do not hear what I say to you."

" Very well, my lord," Falstaff answered, "very well ; rather it is a disease of not listening that I am troubled with."

" I sent for you," said the Lord Chief Justice more sternly, " when there were matters against you which might have brought you to your death, to come and speak with me."

" As I was then advised by my learned counsel," Falstaff replied airily, " I did not come."

" Well, the truth is," went on the Lord Chief Justice, " you live in great infamy."

" A man that has to wear so large a belt as I cannot live in less," replied Falstaff.

" Your means are very slender and your waste is great," said the Lord Chief Justice.

" I wish it were otherwise," sighed Falstaff " I would rather have my means greater and my waist slenderer."

" You have misled the youthful Prince," said the Lord Chief Justice.

" It is the young Prince that misleads me," replied Falstaff.

" You follow the Prince up and down like an evil angel."

" Not so, my lord," Falstaff retorted ; " an evil angel is light. You who are old do not consider the capacities of us who are young."

" What, you call yourself a young man ? Why, everything about you is old. Would you yet call yourself young ? Fie, fie, fie, Sir John ! "

" My lord," replied Falstaff, on his dignity, " I was born about three o'clock in the afternoon, with a white head and a somewhat round belly. My voice—I have lost it in singing anthems. The truth is, I am only old in judgment and understanding."

And on this theme Falstaff let out a torrent of words.

" Well," said the Lord Chief Justice, " God send the Prince a better companion."

" God send the companion a better Prince," replied Falstaff. " I cannot get rid of him."

" Well," again said the Lord Chief Justice,

" the King has separated you and Prince Harry, for I hear you are going with Prince John of Lancaster against the Archbishop and the Earl of Northumberland."

" Yes," said Falstaff, " I can thank you for that, but I pray that our armies do not fight on a hot day, for I only take two shirts with me, and I do not mean to sweat extraordinarily. There is not a dangerous action but I am thrust into it. Well, I cannot last for ever; but it was always the trick of our English nation, if they have a good thing, to make it too common. If you say that I am an old man you should give me rest. I would to God my name were not so terrible to the enemy as it is."

" Well, be honest, be honest, and God bless your expedition," said the Lord Chief Justice affably.

At this change of tone, Falstaff came and stood beside the Lord Chief Justice. Then he said very pleasantly, " Will your lordship lend me a thousand pounds to equip me ? "

" Not a penny, not a penny," retorted the Lord Chief Justice. " Fare you well, and commend me to my good cousin the Earl of Westmoreland."

So the Lord Chief Justice went on his way, leaving Falstaff indignant at his meanness.

" Boy," he said to the page, " what money is there in my purse ? "

" Seven groats and twopence," replied the page.

" I can get no remedy against this consumption of the purse," grumbled Falstaff ; " borrowing only prolongs it ; the disease is incurable."

Falstaff was soon in trouble for his borrowings. From Mistress Quickly, hostess of the Boar's Head Tavern, he had already borrowed much and paid back nothing. Even she was so tired of his promises at last that she paid the fees of the officers and brought them to arrest Sir John.

As Falstaff, Bardolph, and the boy were coming down the street Mistress Quickly saw them, and urged the officers to do their duty. They stepped forward and cried, " Sir John, we arrest you at the suit of Mistress Quickly." Falstaff resisted. Mistress Quickly became very excited and called for help, and there might soon have been a riot had not the Lord Chief Justice passed that way. He called on them to keep the peace, and then he asked what was the matter.

" Oh, my most worshipful lord, if it please your Grace, I am a poor widow of Eastcheap, and he is arrested at my suit," Mistress Quickly replied.

" For what sum ? " asked the Lord Chief Justice.

" It is more than for some," she cried, " it is for all, all I have ; he has eaten me out of house and home ; he has put all my substance into that fat belly of his ; but I'll have some of it out again."

The Lord Chief Justice rebuked Falstaff.

" Are you not ashamed," he said sternly, " to force a poor widow to take this course to get her own ? "

" What is the full sum I owe you ? " asked Falstaff loftily.

" If you were an honest man," she replied, " yourself, and the money too. You swore to me on a silver gilt goblet, sitting in my chamber, called the Dolphin chamber, at the round table, by a coal fire on Wednesday in Witsun week, when the Prince broke your head for saying his father was like a singing man of Windsor ; you swore to me then, as I was washing your wound, to marry me and make me my lady your wife. Can you deny it ? Did not goodwife Keech, the butcher's wife, come in then and call me Gossip Quickly ? Coming in to borrow a mess of vinegar, telling us she had a good dish of prawns ; whereby you desired to eat some ; whereby I told you they were ill for a raw wound. And did you not, when she was gone downstairs, desire me to be less familiar with such poor people, saying that before long they would call me madam ? And did you not kiss me and bid me fetch you thirty shillings. I put you now to your book oath ; deny it if you can."

" My lord," said Falstaff smoothly, " this is a poor mad soul. And she says up and down the town that her eldest son is like you. The truth is, poverty has distracted her. But as for these foolish officers, I beseech you I may have redress against them."

"Sir John, Sir John," said the Lord Chief Justice, "I am well acquainted with your manner of wrenching the true cause the false way; I know you sponge upon the easy nature of this woman and make her serve your purpose."

"My lord," said Falstaff with great dignity, "I will not endure this rebuke without reply. You call honourable boldness impudent sauciness. If a man will bow and say nothing, he is virtuous. No, my lord, I will not ask you for favours. I say I desire to be delivered from these officers, for I am on hasty business of the King's."

"You answer as if you had power to do wrong," said the Lord Chief Justice; "but remember your reputation, and satisfy the poor woman."

Falstaff, seeing that there was no better remedy, beckoned to Mistress Quickly, and said loftily, "Come hither, hostess."

Then he whispered in her ear, promising once again that he would pay her, but in the meantime begging her to lend him ten pounds.

Mistress Quickly was always a great admirer of Sir John, but she knew him of old, and ten pounds was more than she could find. She was reluctant.

"As I am a gentleman," pleaded Falstaff.

"Yes, you said so before," replied Mistress Quickly.

"As I am a gentleman," Falstaff repeated. "Come, no more words about it."

"By this heavenly ground I tread on," said Mistress Quickly, "I must pawn my plate and tapestry in my dining chambers to raise it."

"The best people use glasses," Falstaff answered, "and on your walls some pretty picture, or the story of the Prodigal Son, or a German hunting scene, is worth a thousand of these fly-bitten tapestries. Come, if it was not for your whims, there is not a better wench in England. Go and wash your face and withdraw your action. Come, you must not be in this humour with me. Come now, I know some one has set you on to it."

Mistress Quickly was yielding, as she always had yielded, to Falstaff's persuasions.

"I pray you, Sir John," she said pathetically, "let it be but twenty nobles * ; truly, I am loath to pawn my plate."

Falstaff looked at her sadly. Then he said reproachfully, "Let it alone ; I will make some other arrangement. You will always be a fool."

"Well," at last she replied, "you shall have it, if I have to pawn my gown. I hope you will come to supper."

"Will I live!" exclaimed Falstaff.

"Will you have Doll Tearsheet meet you at supper?" she asked.

"No more words," said Falstaff, "let's have her."

---

* A noble was worth 6s. 8d.

So Falstaff and the hostess were once more reconciled, and as usual, she had the worst of the bargain.

When Prince Henry heard of the supper party, and how Doll Tearsheet was to sup there, he said to Poins, " How could we see Falstaff as he truly is, and not ourselves be seen ? "

Poins replied, " Let us put on leather coats and aprons, and we'll wait upon him at his table as if we were drawers."

When evening came, Falstaff supped with his friends. All ate and drank so heartily that when Mistress Quickly and Doll Tearsheet left the dining-room both were somewhat flushed. Falstaff followed them singing. He sat down on one of the stools and Doll sat by him. She was feeling sad at his departure.

" Come," she said, " I'll be friends with you, Jack. You're going to the wars, and whether I shall ever see you again or not, nobody cares."

One of the drawers came in to say that Ancient Pistol was below and wished to speak with Falstaff. Doll Tearsheet could not bear this Pistol, who was a bullying coward and a great talker.

" Swaggering rogue ! " she cried ; " don't let him come here. He has the foulest mouth of any rogue in England ! "

At the word swagger Mistress Quickly became anxious.

" If he swaggers," she said, " don't let him

come here ; no, by my faith, I must live among my neighbours. I'll have no swaggerers here. I have a good name. Shut the door. There come no swaggerers here. I have not lived all this time to have swaggering now. Shut the door ! "

Falstaff insisted that he should be allowed to come in.

" He is my Ancient," he said. " He is no swaggerer ; just a tame cheater ; you may stroke him as gently as a baby greyhound. Come, call him up, drawer."

Pistol climbed the stairs with Bardolph and the boy. Pistol was ferocious to look at, and his words were very mighty, for he used often to go to the Playhouses, and he liked to speak like a ranting actor.

As soon as he saw Doll they began to abuse each other. Falstaff stopped them.

" No more, Pistol ! " he said. " I would not have you go off here ; discharge yourself out of our company."

" No, not here," added Mistress Quickly, " not here, sweet captain."

" Captain ! " screamed Doll contemptuously, " you abominable cheater ! are you not ashamed to be called captain ? Why, you should be set upon with a truncheon for taking the name of captain before you have earned it ! You a captain ! For what ? "

Bardolph began to fear that there would be a

brawl. He begged Pistol to leave the room and go downstairs, but Pistol was angry and looking for trouble. He began to repeat his play scraps, which seemed very learned to the hostess.

" Begone," said Bardolph, " this will grow to a brawl soon."

" Die men like dogs ! Give crowns like pins ! Have we not Hiren here ? " ranted Pistol.

" Pistol, I would be quiet," said Falstaff.

" Sweet knight," went on Pistol, " I kiss thy fist : What ? We have seen the Seven Stars."

" For goodness' sake," cried Doll, " thrust him downstairs. I cannot endure such a shabby rogue ! "

" Thrust him downstairs ? " flashed Pistol.

" Thrust him down, Bardolph," said Falstaff, who was growing angry.

" Come on," said Bardolph, " get downstairs."

" What ! " cried Pistol ; " shall we fight ? Then Death rock me asleep, abridge my doleful days ! Why, then, let grievous, ghastly, gaping wounds untwine the Sisters Three. Come, Atropos, I say ! " and he began to brandish his rapier.

Falstaff was roused.

" Give me my rapier, boy ! " he cried. Then drawing his own sword he went heavily after Pistol, crying out, " Get you downstairs ! "

Pistol was in no mood for a fight, especially when he saw that Falstaff was in earnest. He made a thrust or two and then disappeared through the door.

Doll Tearsheet was full of admiration.

"I pray you, Jack," she said, "be quiet ; the rascal's gone. Oh, you little valiant villain ! "

"Are you hurt ? " asked Mistress Quickly. " I thought he made a shrewd thrust at you."

When Bardolph returned, Falstaff asked, " Have you turned him out of doors ? "

"Yes," replied Bardolph. "The rascal's drunk ; you have hurt him in the shoulder."

"A rascal, to brave me ! " said Falstaff.

Doll perched herself on Falstaff's knee again, and pacified him.

"Oh, you sweet little rogue, you ! " she said lovingly. " Poor ape, how you sweat. Come, let me wipe your face. Ah, you rogue, truly I love you ; you are as full of valour as Hector of Troy, worth five of Agamemnon, and ten times better than the Nine Worthies.* Oh, villain ! "

"The rascally knave," muttered Falstaff. " I will toss the rogue in a blanket."

The musicians who had been ordered to come and play to the party entered. Doll put her arms round Falstaff's neck. His mind was still on Pistol.

"A rascal bragging slave ! " he murmured. " The rogue fled from me like quicksilver."

---

* Nine prominent men in the history of London described by Richard Johnson (1592).

" And you followed him like a church," said Doll. " You little Bartholomew porker, when will you leave fighting and begin to patch up your old body for heaven ? "

"Peace, Doll!" said Falstaff; "do not speak like a death's head ; do not remind me of my end."

The Prince and Poins, dressed like drawers, came in quietly and stood behind Falstaff. Doll recognized them. She said nothing to Falstaff, but began to egg him on.

" Tell me," she asked him, " what is the Prince like ? "

" Oh," replied Falstaff loftily, " a shallow young man ; he would have made a good pantry man, and he would have cut bread well."

" They say Poins has a good wit," went on Doll Tearsheet.

" He, a good wit ? " Falstaff said contemptuously, " hang him, the baboon ! his wit's as thick as Tewkesbury mustard ; there's no more cleverness in him than in a mallet."

" Then why does the Prince like him ? "

" Oh," said Falstaff, " because their legs are the same size. He plays quoits well, behaves wildly, jumps upon stools well, swears well, wears his boots very smooth, and he has other qualities that show a weak mind and an able body. So the Prince employs him, for the Prince himself is much the same ; the weight of a hair will turn the scales either way."

" Would not this nave of a wheel have his ears cut off ? " whispered the Prince to Poins.

" Let's beat him," replied Poins, " before his girl."

" Kiss me, Doll," said Falstaff sentimentally.

She kissed him eagerly, and he was greatly flattered.

" I am old, I am old," Falstaff murmured.

" I love you more than I love a scurvy youth," Doll answered.

Falstaff was moved.

" What stuff will you have a gown made of ? " he asked. " I shall have money on Thursday. You shall have a cap to-morrow. But come, let us have a merry song ; it grows late, so we will go to bed. You will forget me when I am gone."

" Truly," said Doll, " you'll make me weep if you say so. I won't dress myself pretty until you come back."

" Some sack, Francis," Falstaff called to the drawer.

" Coming, sir," answered the Prince and Poins together.

" Ha ! " cried Falstaff when he saw them. " One of the King's disreputable sons ? And are you not Poins his brother ? "

Then the Prince pretended to be very angry with Falstaff for abusing him.

" Did you hear me ? " asked Falstaff, a little anxiously.

" Yes," replied the Prince, " and you knew me, as you did when you ran away that night of the robbery ; you knew I was at your back and spoke it on purpose to try my patience."

" No, no, no," said Falstaff, " not so. I did not think you were within hearing."

" I shall drive you then," said the Prince fiercely, " to confess the abuse."

" No abuse, Hal," said Falstaff, shaking his head ; " on my honour, no abuse."

" Not to dispraise me, and call me a pantry man, and I know not what ? " said the Prince.

" No abuse, Hal," said Falstaff again.

" No abuse ? " said Poins in amazement.

" No abuse, Ned, none," said Falstaff. " I dispraised him before the wicked that the wicked might not fall in love with him ; in so doing I have done the part of a careful friend and true subject, and your father should give me thanks for it. No abuse, Hal , none, Ned, none."

" See now," said the Prince, " whether pure fear and entire cowardice does not make you wrong this virtuous gentlewoman. Is she one of the wicked ? Is your hostess here of the wicked ? Or is your boy of the wicked ? Or honest Bardolph, whose zeal burns in his nose, of the wicked ? "

" Answer, you dead elm, answer ! " said Poins.

" The fiend," said Falstaff slowly, " has pricked down Bardolph irrecoverable ; and his face is

Lucifer's private kitchen, where he does nothing but roast malt-worms. For the boy, there is a good angel about him, but the devil outbids him too."

" And the women ? " asked the Prince.

" One of them is in hell already," said Falstaff. " The other, I owe her money, and whether she is damned for that, I do not know."

" No, I warrant you ! " cried Mistress Quickly.

" No," agreed Falstaff, " I think you are not ; I think you are forgiven for that."

But their talk was interrupted and there was a loud knocking at the door.

Messengers were seeking the Prince and Falstaff, for bad news had come from the north that the rebels were on the march. Falstaff bade farewell to the hostess and went off to do his duty.

So Falstaff set out once more with Bardolph to collect another company and to serve his king and himself. He remembered an old acquaintance called Justice Shallow. He had known Shallow when they were young men together in London. Shallow in those days was a feeble little creature, so thin that he looked like a radish, on which some one had carved a face. This Shallow had now become a great man in a little way in Gloucestershire. So Falstaff wrote to him, bidding him call up recruits, whom he would inspect on his way to the wars. Justice Shallow was eager to show his zeal as a country magistrate. He summoned half a dozen likely men from the nearest town and waited for Falstaff.

When Falstaff arrived the recruits were all ready, each hoping that one of the others would be chosen. Falstaff sat down with Justice Shallow and his neighbour, Justice Silence. Justice Shallow fussily produced the roll and unfolded it. " Let me see," he said, " let me see, let me see. So, so, so, so, so, so, so. Yes, indeed. Ralph Mouldy ! Where is Mouldy ? "

He looked at the unwilling recruits.

" Here, if it please you," said Mouldy, stepping forward.

" What do you think, Sir John ? " said Shallow. " A good limbed fellow, young, strong, and of good friends."

" Is your name Mouldy ? " asked Falstaff.

" Yes, and it please you," repeated Mouldy.

" It is time you were used," remarked Falstaff. " Prick him."

Shallow marked Mouldy's name on the list.

Mouldy protested. The old woman that he served, he said, had no one else to do her work and to help her. " You need not have pricked me," he added ; " there are other men fitter to go than I."

" You shall go," said Falstaff ; " it is time you were spent."

Mouldy was disposed to argue, but Justice

Shallow impatiently told him to stand aside. Then he called the name of Simon Shadow.

" Yes," said Falstaff, " let me have him to sit under ; he is likely to be a cold soldier."

So Shadow also was pricked down. Then Thomas Wart was called up. He was a very ragged recruit, for most of his clothing hung together with pins. Next Francis Feeble stepped forward.

" What trade are you, Feeble ? " asked Falstaff.

" A woman's tailor, sir."

" Shall I prick him, sir ? " Shallow inquired.

" You may," said Falstaff ; " but if he had been a man's tailor he would have pricked you. Will you make as many holes in an enemy's battle as you have done in a woman's petticoat ? "

" I will do my best, sir," said Feeble.

" Well said, courageous Feeble ! " exclaimed Falstaff. " You will be as valiant as the wrathful dove or most magnanimous mouse. Prick the woman's tailor, Master Shallow, deep, Master Shallow."

" I wish Wart might have gone, sir," Feeble suggested.

" I wish you were a man's tailor," replied Falstaff, " that you might mend him and make him fit to go. Let that suffice, most forcible Feeble."

" It shall suffice, sir," said Feeble, stepping back.

" Who's next ? " asked Falstaff.

" Peter Bullcalf," said Shallow.

" Let's see Bullcalf then," said Falstaff.

So Bullcalf stepped forward.

" A likely fellow," remarked Falstaff. " Come, prick him till he roar again."

But Bullcalf was not disposed to go.

" Oh, lord ! good my lord captain——" he began.

" What," said Falstaff, " do you roar before you are pricked ? "

" Oh, lord, sir ! " said Bullcalf, " I am a diseased man."

" What disease have you ? " asked Falstaff.

" A cold, sir, a cough, sir, which I caught with ringing in the King's affairs upon his coronation day, sir."

" Come," said Falstaff, " you shall go to the wars in a gown ; we'll put an end to your cold. I will arrange for your friends to ring for you. Is that all ? " he asked, turning to Shallow.

" There are two more called than your number ; you must have but four here, sir ; but let us go in to dinner."

" I will drink with you," said Falstaff, " but I cannot wait for dinner. I am glad to see you though, Master Shallow."

" Oh, Sir John," said Shallow, very flattered, " do you remember when we lay all night in the windmill in Saint George's field ? " For he was excited to see his old companion, and the more so as he wished to impress his neighbour Silence, who had heard many tales of Justice Shallow's gay youth in London.

" No more of that," said Falstaff, " no more of that."

" Ha ! " went on Shallow ; " it was a merry night. And is Jane Nightwork alive ? "

" She lives, Master Shallow," said Falstaff curtly, for he did not wish too much of his own past to be dragged out.

" She could never abide me," said Shallow.

" No," said Falstaff, " she would always say she never could."

" By the Mass," said Shallow, " I could anger her to the heart. Does she hold her own well ? "

" Old, old, Master Shallow."

" No, she must be old," said Shallow ; " she cannot choose but be old ; certain she's old ; her boy, Robin Nightwork, was born before I came to Clement's Inn."

" That's fifty-five years ago," said Justice Silence, who knew Shallow's stories almost by heart.

" Ha ! cousin Silence," said Shallow, " if only you had seen what we have seen ! Ha ! Sir John, said I well ? "

" We have heard the chimes at midnight, Master Shallow," replied Falstaff gravely.

" That we have, that we have, that we have ! "
said Shallow. " Truly, Sir John, we have ; come,
let's go in to dinner ; oh, the days that we have
seen ! Come, come."

So the two Justices and Sir John went in to
dinner, leaving the recruits with Bardolph.
Bullcalf shuffled up to Bardolph and whispered :
" Good Master Corporate Bardolph, stand by
me : here's four Harry ten shillings. Truly, sir, I
would rather be hanged than go ; and yet, for
my own part, sir, I do not care ; but I have a
desire to stay with my friends ; else, sir, I do not
care for my own part so much."

Bardolph took the money.

" So be it," he said, " stand aside."

Mouldy also had his petition to make.

" Good Master Corporal Captain," he whined,
" for my old lady's sake, be my friend ; she has
nobody to do anything for her when I am gone ;
and she is old, and can't help herself ; you shall
have forty, sir."

" So be it," said Bardolph, " stand aside."

Feeble was contemptuous of such unmanly
behaviour.

" I don't care," he said. " A man can die but
once. We owe God a death. I'll never have a
base mind. If it be my destiny, so ; if it be not,
so. No man is too good to serve his Prince ; and
whatever happens, he that dies this year has paid
for the next."

" Well said," said Bardolph, " you are a good fellow."

" I'll have no base mind," repeated Feeble valiantly.

When Falstaff came back, he said to Shallow : " Come, sir, which men shall I have ? "

" Sir, a word with you," whispered Bardolph. " I have three pounds to free Mouldy and Bullcalf."

" So be it," Falstaff nodded.

" Come, Sir John," said Shallow, " which four will you have ? "

" Choose for me," said Falstaff.

" Why then, Mouldy, Bullcalf, Feeble, and Shadow."

Falstaff looked at Mouldy and Bullcalf, and said : " For you, Mouldy, stay at home till you are past service. And for your part, Bullcalf, grow till you come to it ; I will have none of you."

" Sir John, Sir John," protested Shallow, " you do yourself wrong ; they are your likeliest men, and I would that you had the best."

Falstaff turned on the little Justice haughtily. " Will you tell me, Master Shallow, how to choose a man ? Do I care for the limb, the thews, the stature, the bulk of a man ! Give me the spirit, Master Shallow. Here's Wart ; you see what a ragged appearance he has, yet he'll strike as quick as a pewterer's hammer. And this half-faced fellow Shadow ; he presents no mark to the

enemy ; the foe may with as great aim level at
the edge of a penknife. And for a retreat ; how
swiftly will this Feeble, the woman's tailor, run
off ! Oh, give me the spare men, and spare me
the great ones. Put a musket into Wart's hand,
Bardolph."

Bardolph gave Wart a musket and put him
through his motions. Shallow shook his head.
In the good old days, when he was at Clement's
Inn, they did things better.

" These fellows will do well, Master Shallow,"
said Falstaff.

He bade the two Justices farewell. Shallow
took his hand.

" At your return," he said, " visit our house ;
let our old acquaintance be renewed. I wish I
might go with you to Court."

" I would that you could," said Falstaff.

Bardolph collected the recruits, and Falstaff
went on his way northward. He was in time for
the battle, and there did good service, for in the
rout of the rebels he had the luck to take prisoner
a rebel knight called Sir John Colville. The war
being thus quickly ended, the army was dis-
charged, and all the soldiers made their way home
as fast as they could.

Falstaff decided that he would go back by way
of Gloucestershire and pay another visit to Master
Shallow, thinking that so simple a gentleman
would be easy prey. Shallow was very excited to

see him once more, for few visitors from the great world of London came his way. Falstaff enjoyed himself greatly, and soon the little Justice was persuaded that with Falstaff's aid he would himself become a great man.

They were discussing this matter over supper. It was a warm night. After supper they went out to sit in the orchard in the cool of the evening. There were five of them, Falstaff and the two Justices, Silence and Shallow, Bardolph, and the boy. They had supped well and drank well, so that the two Justices were inclined to be merry. Justice Silence was very noisy, and every now and then would break into song. Davy, Shallow's man, brought out apples and wine. Thus they went on drinking to each other and were prepared to make a merry night of it.

Suddenly they were interrupted. Davy came in to say that one called Pistol had come from the Court with news.

" From the Court ? " said Falstaff. " Let him come in."

There was one piece of news that Falstaff was expecting and eagerly awaiting. Before he set out north it was known that King Henry IV. was dangerously ill.

" Well, Pistol ? " said Falstaff.

" Sir John ! " cried Pistol, " God save you ! "

" What wind blew you here, Pistol ? " asked Falstaff.

" Not the ill wind which blows no man to good,"
answered Pistol in his ranting way. " Sweet
knight, you are now one of the greatest men in
this realm."

" I think so too," murmured Silence. " I
think he is as great as Goodman Puff of Barson."

" Puff ! " exclaimed Pistol indignantly, " Puff
in your teeth, most recreant coward base ! Sir
John, I am thy Pistol and thy friend, and helter-
skelter I have ridden to thee, and tidings do I
bring and lucky joys and golden times and happy
news of price."

Falstaff was used to Pistol's way of speaking,
but just now he wanted a plain tale.

" I pray you," he said, " tell your news like a
man of this world."

" A fig for the world," cried Pistol, excitedly
snapping his fingers. " I speak of Africa and
golden joys."

Falstaff fell in with his mood and answered
him.

" Oh, base Assyrian knight, what is thy news ?
Let King Cophetua know the truth thereof."

" And Robin Hood, Scarlet, and John,"
mumbled Silence as he fell asleep, and disappeared under the table.

" Shall dunghill curs confront the Helicons,"
ranted Pistol. " Shall good news be baffled ?
Then, Pistol, lay thy head in Furies' lap."

This was Greek to Shallow, who had never met

any one of Pistol's kind before. He was greatly puzzled.

" Honest gentleman," he said, " I do not know your breeding."

" Why, then, lament therefore," replied Pistol.

" I beg your pardon, sir," said Shallow, " but if you come with news from the Court, I take it there is but two ways ; either to utter it, or conceal it. I am, sir, under the King in some authority," he added proudly.

" Under which king ? " retorted Pistol.

" Under King Harry."

" Harry the Fourth or Fifth ? "

" Harry the Fourth."

" A fig for your office ! " exclaimed Pistol. " Sir John, your tender lambkin is now king ; Harry the Fifth's the man. I speak the truth."

" What," said Falstaff starting up, " is the old king dead ? "

" As nail in door," Pistol replied.

Falstaff rose to his feet. " Saddle my horses," he cried. " Choose what office you will in the land, it is yours."

" What ! I bring good news," said Pistol.

" Carry Master Silence to bed," said Falstaff. Then to Shallow, who was still bewildered, but realized that something very important had happened, he added : " My Lord Shallow, you can have any title you want, it is yours for the asking. Get on your boots ; we'll ride all night. Sweet

Pistol ! Away, Bardolph ! I know the young king is sick for me. Let us take any man's horses. The laws of England are at my command. Blessed are they that have been my friends ; and woe to my Lord Chief Justice ! "

All was bustle in Shallow's house. The old Justice was as excited as the others, and was easily persuaded by Falstaff's glib promises to lend him a thousand pounds. Soon their horses were ready and they rode all night. When at last they reached London, it was to learn that King Henry the Fifth was even then being crowned in Westminster Abbey. They took their places where the procession would pass on its way back to the palace, and where the king must see them.

" Stand by me here, Master Robert Shallow," said Falstaff. " I will make the King honour you. I will leer upon him as he comes by, and then note how he will look upon me. Come here, Pistol, come behind me. If only I had had time to get new clothes made, I would have spent the thousand pounds I borrowed from you," he said to Shallow. " But no matter, this poor show does better ; it shows the zeal I had to see him."

" It does indeed," said Shallow.

" It shows my earnestness of affection——"

" It does," said Shallow.

" My devotion——"

" It does, it does, it does."

" As it were, to ride day and night," Falstaff

went on, "not to waste time to change my clothes."

"It is best certainly," said Shallow.

"But to stand stained with travel, and sweating with desire to see him ; thinking of nothing else, putting all other affairs aside, as if there were nothing else to be done but to see him."

There was a roar of cheering as the King came out of the Abbey. He passed by with the nobles attending him, amongst them the Lord Chief Justice.

"God save your Grace, King Hal ! My royal Hal ! " cried Falstaff, waving his cap.

"The heavens thee guard and keep, most royal imp of fame ! " shouted Pistol.

"God save you, my sweet boy ! " Falstaff cried.

The new King paused. His nobles were watching him curiously to see how he would answer. The King looked at Falstaff ; in a moment Falstaff saw that something had gone wrong.

"My Lord Chief Justice," said the King severely, "speak to that vain man."

The Lord Chief Justice went up to Falstaff.

"Are you out of your wits," he said, "do you know what you say ? "

Falstaff ignored him.

"My King ! I speak to you, my heart ! " again he cried, although he was feeling more and more uneasy.

The King spoke more sternly. " Old man," he said, " I do not know you. Get to your prayers. I have long dreamed of such a man, so swollen, so old, and so profane ; but being awake I despise my dream. Do not reply to me with some foolish jest. Do not presume to think that I am the thing I was ; for God knows, and soon the world shall know too, that I have turned away from my past life and my old companions. When you hear that I am as I have been, come near me ; and you shall be as you were, the tutor and feeder of my riots ; but until then I banish you, on pain of death. I will allow you means to live, and as I hear you reform so I will give you promotion."

With these words the King bade the procession pass on. When all had gone by, Falstaff, very subdued, turned to Shallow and said quietly,

" Master Shallow, I owe you a thousand pounds."

" Yes," said Shallow sadly, who had now realized how grievously he had been mistaken in his old acquaintance ; " and I beg you let me have some of it to take home with me."

" That can hardly be," said Falstaff, as his old optimism began to return. " But do not grieve at this. I shall be sent for privately. He must appear as he does to the world ; but do not fear your promotion. I will be the man yet that will make you great."

" I cannot well perceive how," said Shallow sourly, " unless you should give me your doublet and stuff me out with straw. I beseech you, Sir John," he pleaded, " let me have five hundred of my thousand."

" Sir," said Falstaff, " I will be as good as my word ; what you heard now was a pretence."

They were about to go, when Prince John and the Lord Chief Justice met them with his men.

" Take Sir John Falstaff to the Fleet Prison," he commanded. " And take all his company with him."

" My lord, my lord——" Falstaff protested.

" Take them away," said the Lord Chief Justice impatiently.

So Falstaff, Justice Shallow, and the rest spent the night in prison. But they were soon released, and Justice Shallow went back to Gloucestershire a wiser and much poorer man. As for Falstaff, he returned to his old haunts ; but it was soon seen that the gaiety had gone out of him. He knew in himself, though he would never admit it, that the old days were over, and now that Prince Hal was King he had banished his wild companions for ever.

Soon the news came that there would be wars in France. Bardolph and Pistol were excited, for war meant plunder. But Falstaff's wars were ended ; he did not go with them. He pined and took to his bed. His old friends came to see him.

It was too late. When they reached the Boar's Head Tavern Mistress Quickly told them that he was dead.

"Would that I were with him," moaned Bardolph, "wherever he is, either in heaven or in hell."

"No, sure, he's not in hell," said Mistress Quickly. "He's in Arthur's bosom, if ever man went to Arthur's bosom; and he made a finer end, and went away as if he had been an innocent. He departed even just between twelve and one, even at the turning of the tide; for after I saw him fumble with the sheets, and play with flowers, and smile upon his fingers' end, I knew there was but one way: for his nose was as sharp as a pen, and he babbled of green fields. 'How now, Sir John,' I said, 'be of good cheer.' So he cried out, 'God, God, God' three or four times. I, to comfort him, told him not to think of God just yet; I hoped there was no need to trouble himself with any such thoughts yet. So he bade me lay more clothes on his feet. I put my hand into the bed and felt them, and they were as cold as any stone. Then I felt to his knees, and so upward, and upward, and all was as cold as any stone."

"They say he cried out of sack," said one of them.

"Yes, that he did," said Mistress Quickly.

"And of women," added Bardolph.

" No, that he did not," she replied indignantly.

" Oh yes, he did," interrupted the page, " and said they were devils incarnate."

" Why," said Mistress Quickly, " he could never abide carnation, it was a colour he never liked."

" Do you remember," went on the boy, " how he saw a flea stick on Bardolph's nose, and he said it was a black soul burning in Hell ? "

" Well," replied Bardolph gloomily, " the fuel is gone that maintained that fire ; that's all the riches I got in his service."

So that was the end of Falstaff.

II

MUCH ADO ABOUT NOTHING

THE city of Messina was once governed by a nobleman called Leonato. Leonato had a daughter
called Hero, and a niece called Beatrice, who was
an orphan and lived in his household.

One day there came a letter to Leonato that
Don Pedro, Prince of Arragon, was on his way to
the city. The Prince was returning from the
wars after a short campaign, in which he had
beaten the enemy so handsomely that few had
fallen on either side. With Don Pedro were
coming many of his officers, amongst them
Claudio and Benedick. Claudio was half in love
with Hero, and she with him. Benedick and
Beatrice professed to hate each other, and indeed
all of the opposite sex, so that these two could
never come together but they must fall into
wrangling and a wordy warfare in which each
tried to overthrow the other.

Leonato and the ladies asked for news of the

gentlemen. Claudio, said the messenger, had won great honour in the war.

Beatrice inquired after Benedick.

" I pray you," said she, " how many has he killed and eaten in these wars ? for I promised to eat all of his killing."

" He has done good service, lady," the messenger replied.

"Yes," said Beatrice, " you had stale victuals, and he helped to eat them. He is a very valiant eater."

Soon afterwards Don Pedro arrived. Claudio and Benedick were with him, as well as Don John, his half-brother, and Balthasar, another of his gentlemen. The Prince greeted Leonato very eagerly and accepted his invitation to stay in his house. Then the two ladies, Hero and Beatrice, were introduced to him, and soon the whole house was noisy with the conversation as the soldiers told their news. Beatrice and Benedick were quickly drawn together, and their old warfare broke out at once.

" I wonder," Beatrice remarked, " that you will still be talking, Signior Benedick ; nobody listens to you."

" What ? " said Benedick, as if he had not noticed her before, " my dear Lady Disdain ! Are you still living ? "

The Prince called to Claudio and Benedick and said, " Signior Claudio and Signior Benedick, my dear friend Leonato has invited you all. I tell him we shall stay here at least a month, and he hopes that something will keep us longer."

Then Leonato spoke to Don John, bidding him welcome too, and especially since he was reconciled to his brother the Prince after a long quarrel.

" I thank you," muttered Don John.   " I am not a man of many words, but I thank you."

Claudio then took Benedick by the arm and led him away.   He looked serious.

" Benedick," he asked, " did you note the daughter of Signior Leonato ? "

" I did not take great note of her," Benedick replied.

" Is she not a modest young lady ? " said Claudio.

Benedick saw what was in Claudio's mind.

" Do you question me as an honest man should, for my simple true judgment ?   Or would you have me speak, after my custom, as a professed hater of women ? "

" No," answered Claudio ;   " I pray you speak in sober judgment."

" Well," said Benedick critically, " I think she is too low for a high praise, too brown for fair praise, and too little for great praise.   Only I will commend her thus far, that if she were different from what she is she would be unhandsome, but as she is, I do not like her."

" You think I am jesting," said Claudio ;   " I pray you, tell me truthfully how you like her."

Benedick looked at him closely.

" Would you buy her that you ask after her ? "

" Can the world buy such a jewel ? " asked Claudio.

" Yes, and a case to put it into," Benedick answered.

" In my eye," said Claudio fervently, " she is the sweetest lady that I ever looked on."

" I can see without spectacles," said Benedick, " and I see no such matter." Then he added suspiciously, " I hope you have no intent to turn husband, have you ? "

" If Hero would be my wife," Claudio replied.

Benedick shook his head very sadly, " Is it come to this ? Shall I never see a bachelor of sixty again ? "

Don Pedro came back to look for them. He saw them whispering together, and asked what secret kept them there that they had not followed him.

" I wish your Grace would command me to tell you," answered Benedick.

" I charge you on your allegiance," said the Prince with mock severity.

" You hear, Count Claudio ? " said Benedick. " I can be secret as a dumb man, you must believe that ; but I am charged on my allegiance." Then very scornfully he said to the Prince, " He is in love."

" With whom ? " asked Don Pedro.

" With Hero, Leonato's daughter."

" Well," said the Prince, " the lady is very worthy."

" You speak thus to mock me, my lord," Claudio answered.

" No, indeed," said Don Pedro. " I speak what I think."

" Indeed, my lord, I say what I think too," said Claudio. " I love her."

" I know she is worthy," the Prince replied.

" As for me," said Benedick, " I neither feel how she should be loved, nor do I know how she could be worthy, and I would die at the stake for that."

" You were ever a heretic in such matters," said Don Pedro.

" That a woman was my mother," said Benedick, " I thank her. As she brought me up, likewise I give her most humble thanks ; but for anything further, all women must pardon me, because I will not wrong them by mistrusting any. Therefore I will trust none ; and the end is, I will live a bachelor."

" Before I die," Don Pedro answered, " I will see you look pale with love."

Benedick was horrified at such a thought. " With sickness or with hunger, my lord, not with love."

" Well," said Don Pedro, " time will show. ' In time the savage bull doth bear the yoke.' "

" The savage bull may," replied Benedick,

" but if ever the sensible Benedick does, pluck off the bull's horns and set them upon my forehead ; and let a vile picture of me be painted, and underneath it in great letters write, ' HERE YOU MAY SEE BENEDICK THE MARRIED MAN.' "

" If Cupid has not used all his arrows," said Don Pedro, " you will suffer for this before long."

" Then we may expect an earthquake," Benedick answered.

The Prince sent Benedick to Leonato's with a message. When he had gone, Claudio began to confide in Don Pedro and to ask his advice. The Prince saw where his thoughts lay, and asked him whether he was in love with Hero.

" My lord," he answered, " when we set out for the wars I looked at Hero with a soldier's eye. I liked her, but had a rougher task in hand. Now that I have returned and the thoughts of war have gone, there come soft and delicate desires all telling me how fair Hero is, reminding me how much I liked her."

" You will talk like a lover soon," said the Prince. " If you love Hero, I will open the question with her and with her father, and you shall have her. Was this not the matter you wished to speak to me about ? "

Claudio was grateful to the Prince for so quickly seeing the drift of his talk. Then the Prince said there would be dancing that night, when all the dancers should wear masks.

" I will pretend to be you," he added, " and then I will tell her how I love her, and after that I will speak to her father, and the end shall be that she will be yours."

All this time Don John, the Prince's brother, had brooded over his wrongs so long that his whole nature was warped. He was consumed with envy, and the only joy in his life was to work mischief. In this he was well aided by two of his servants, called Conrade and Borachio. The gaiety in Leonato's house only made Don John more bitter. He was even angry that his brother should have forgiven him, for he felt that henceforth everything he did would be suspected. Conrade tried to drive away his melancholy, but only the thought of mischief could make him cheerful.

" If I had my liking," Don John grumbled, " I would bite. If I had my liberty I would do what I liked. Meantime, let me be as I am, and do not try to alter me."

Borachio joined them. He had news, he said, of a marriage.

" Who is the fool that will tie himself to unquietness ? " asked Don John.

" Why, it is your brother's right-hand man," said Borachio.

" Who ?   The exquisite Claudio ? " asked Don John.

" Yes."

" And who ?   Which way does he look ? "

" Why, at Hero, the daughter of Leonato."

" How did you come to know of this ? " asked Don John.

" As I was perfuming a musty room," said Borachio, " the Prince and Claudio came by in talk. I hid behind the curtains, and there I heard them agree that the Prince would woo Hero for himself, and then, having won her, would give her to Claudio."

Don John was pleased at this news, for he saw a chance at least of hurting Claudio. He agreed to go to the feast.

That evening, when the feast was ended, Leonato and the ladies of his house came into the Great Hall, waiting until the gentlemen should join them.   They began to talk of Don John.

" How sourly that gentleman looks," remarked Beatrice ; " I can never see him but I have indigestion for an hour afterwards."

" He is very melancholy," Hero answered.

" He would be an excellent man," Beatrice observed, " who came half-way between him and Benedick. The one is too like an image and says nothing, and the other too like a spoilt child, always prattling. "

" Indeed, niece," said Leonato, " you will never get a husband if you are so bitter of tongue."

" I never want one," Beatrice answered.   " I could never endure a husband with a beard."

" Perhaps you will find one without," said Leonato.

" What should I do with him ? " asked Beatrice. " Dress him in my clothes and make him my waiting-gentlewoman ? A man with a beard is more than a youth ; and a man without a beard is less than a man, and I am for neither."

" Well, niece," said Antonio, who was Hero's uncle, " perhaps you will be ruled by your father ? "

" Yes," interrupted Beatrice, " it is my cousin's duty to curtsy and say, ' Father, as it please you.' Yet for all that, cousin, let him be a handsome man ; or else make another curtsy and say, ' Father, as it please me.' "

" Well, niece," said Leonato, " I hope one day to see you fitted with a husband."

" No, uncle," Beatrice answered ; " I will have none. Adam's sons are my brothers, and I hold it a sin to marry in the family."

The dancers were now approaching, and all the ladies put on their masks to disguise themselves. The gentlemen also wore masks.

Don Pedro came up to Hero and led her away to dance with him. The others took their partners. Beatrice knew Benedick and offered herself to him as partner. In spite of the masks, each recognized the other, but pretended that it was otherwise, and in this way they were able to attack each other more fiercely than ever.

Benedick began to talk about Beatrice. " She is proud," he said, " and gets all her witty sayings from jest books."

" Signior Benedick told you that," answered Beatrice.

" Benedick ? Who is he ? " asked Benedick innocently.

" I am sure you know him well enough," replied Beatrice.

" No, not I."

" Did he never make you laugh ? "

" I pray you, tell me who he is," Benedick replied.

" Why, he is the Prince's jester; a very dull fool," said Beatrice. " The only thing he can do is to invent impossible slanders. Only rogues like him."

" When I know the gentleman," said Benedick, " I will tell him what you say."

" Do," said Beatrice, " do. He'll only make some unpleasant remark or other about me. But if you pay no attention to him, then he will become melancholy and eat no supper ; so there will be a partridge wing saved."

Don John was not dancing. He and Borachio carefully watched the others until he saw Claudio. At last the dancing ceased and the dancers left the hall. Claudio stayed behind anxiously waiting for the Prince. Don John went up to him and pretended that he was Benedick. Here was his chance for mischief.

" Are you not Signior Benedick ? " he asked Claudio.

" You know me well," answered Claudio behind his mask, " I am."

" Signior," said Don John, " you are in great favour with my brother the Prince. He is in love with Hero. I beg you to persuade him against her, for she is no equal for one of his birth."

" How do you know that he loves her ? " asked Claudio anxiously.

" I heard him swear that he was in love."

" So did I too," said Borachio, " and he swore that he would marry her to-night."

With these words Don John and Borachio left Claudio to his thoughts. He was greatly distressed. He believed, for he was a simple youth, that it was true, and that the Prince all this while was treacherously wooing Hero for himself. While he was still brooding on the falseness of men in love, Benedick came up to him. Benedick also had heard that the Prince was wooing Hero for himself.

" The Prince has got your Hero," he said.

" I wish him joy of her," Claudio replied sullenly.

" Did you think the Prince would have served you thus ? " asked Benedick.

" I beg you, go away," said Claudio.

Benedick was amused and mocked him.

"Now you strike like a blind man. The boy stole your meat and you beat the post."

"If you will not leave me, I will leave you," said Claudio, and with that he went moodily away.

"Poor hurt waterfowl!" said Benedick as he watched Claudio. "Now he will creep into the rushes and hide himself."

All the same he was very sore, for Beatrice had hurt him cruelly, and he was not quite sure how far she was jesting or speaking the truth when she said that he was known as the Prince's jester.

Then the Prince himself came in, asking for Claudio.

"In truth, my lord," said Benedick, "I found him here very melancholy. I told him—and I think I told him the truth—that you had won the goodwill of the young lady."

The Prince did not answer to this, but he began to speak of Beatrice.

"Lady Beatrice," he said, "has a quarrel with you. The gentleman who danced with her told her that she is much wronged by you."

"Oh," said Benedick in horror, "she abused me so greatly that even a block of wood would have answered her. She told me, not thinking it was I, that I was the Prince's jester. She said such bitter things about me that I felt like a man with a whole army shooting at him. Every word she utters stabs. I would not marry her though she possessed all that Adam had before he was turned out of Paradise."

" Look," said Don Pedro, " here she comes."

Benedick fled.

Then the others came in, Leonato with Hero and Beatrice, and Claudio following them gloomily.

" I have brought Count Claudio, whom you sent me to seek," said Beatrice.

" Why, Count, why are you so sad ? " asked Don Pedro.

" I am not sad," Claudio answered sulkily.

" How then, sick ? "

" Neither, my lord."

" Here, Claudio," he said, " I have wooed in your name and fair Hero is won. I have spoken to her father, who has given his goodwill. Name the day of marriage, and God give you joy."

Leonato took Hero's hand and laid it in Claudio's.

" Count, take my daughter and her fortunes."

Claudio was utterly confused at this unexpected change and he could say nothing for bewilderment and happiness, and Hero was too bashful to speak.

" Speak, cousin," prompted Beatrice, " and if you cannot, stop his mouth with a kiss."

" Truly, lady," said Don Pedro, " you have a merry heart."

" Yes, my lord," Beatrice answered, " I am thankful for it ; it keeps me from worrying. What a thing this marrying is. Every one is going for it except me, and I must sit in the corner and sigh for a husband."

" Will you have me, lady ? " asked Don Pedro.

" No, my lord," said Beatrice lightly, " unless I might have another husband for working days ; your Grace is too costly to wear every day." And then thinking perhaps that she had gone too far, she added, " But I beseech your Grace pardon me, I was born to speak all mirth, and nothing serious."

So she tripped away and left them.

" A pleasant, spirited lady," observed Don Pedro.

" There is not much melancholy about her," Leonato replied. " She is never sad, except when she sleeps ; and not sad then, for I heard my daughter say that she often dreams of unhappiness and wakes herself with laughing."

" She cannot endure to hear of a husband," said Don Pedro thoughtfully.

" By no means. She mocks all her wooers mercilessly," said Leonato.

" She would be an excellent wife for Benedick," said Don Pedro.

" Oh, my lord," exclaimed Leonato, " if they were married a week they would talk each other mad."

" When will you be married ? " Don Pedro asked Claudio.

" To-morrow, my lord."

" Not until Monday," said Leonato, " and that is but a week hence ; and even so, too short a time to have everything ready."

" Come," said Don Pedro to Claudio, " you are impatient at such a long wait ? I promise you, Claudio, time will not pass dully, for in the meantime I will undertake the greatest of labours. I will bring Signior Benedick and Lady Beatrice to fall in love with each other. I would like to see them married, and I will bring it about if you three will help me."

" My lord," said Leonato, " I am for you, though I have to stay awake ten nights for it."

" And so am I," said Claudio.

" And you too, Hero ? " asked Don Pedro.

" I will do anything, my lord, to help my cousin to a good husband," she answered.

" And Benedick," said Don Pedro, " is not the least hopeful husband that I know. I will teach you, Hero, how to persuade your cousin that she will fall in love with Benedick ; and with the help of you two I will so work on Benedick that, in spite of his wit and unwillingness, he will fall in love with Beatrice. If we can do this we will beat Cupid at his own game."

When Don John heard that Claudio's marriage with Hero had been arranged, he was more melancholy than ever, and he longed for some means to prevent it. Borachio was willing to help him. He had a plan. For a long time he had been friendly with Margaret, Hero's gentlewoman.

" At any hour of the night," he said, " I can persuade her to look out of her lady's chamber window."

" But how will that prevent the marriage ? " asked Don John.

" That," replied Borachio, " you must bring about. Go to the Prince, your brother, and tell him that he has not acted honourably in marrying Claudio—whose worth you must mightily praise —to so dishonoured a woman as Hero."

" What proof can I give them of that ? " asked Don John.

" Proof enough," replied Borachio, " to deceive the Prince, to vex Claudio, to undo Hero, and kill Leonato."

" I will do anything to spite them," snarled Don John.

" Go, then," said Borachio ; " find a fit time to speak to the Prince and Count Claudio alone. Tell them that you know Hero loves me. Pretend to be very zealous for your brother's honour and his friend's reputation who is thus likely to be deceived into marrying one who has given herself to another. They will scarcely believe this with-out evidence. Offer them proof : which shall be to see me at her chamber window talking to her the very night before the wedding ; and, in the meantime, I will so arrange things that Hero shall be absent and her disloyalty shall appear clearly proved."

Don John was so greatly elated at the thought that he would be able to revenge himself on his enemies that he promised Borachio a thousand ducats if he could bring it to pass.

Meanwhile Benedick was feeling very melancholy. He was walking alone in Leonato's garden. He was sad that his friend Claudio should make a fool of himself by falling in love. Once there was a time when Claudio was a good soldier ; when he was interested only in drums and fifes and arms and blunt honest words ; but now his thoughts were of new clothes and poetical phrases.

" May I be so converted ? " he sighed. " I cannot tell ; I think not. I will not swear that love may not turn me into an oyster, but I will take my oath on it that until he make me an oyster he will never make me such a fool ; until all graces be in one woman, one woman shall not come into my grace."

He turned, and saw Leonato, the Prince, and Claudio coming down the garden path. He had no wish for further talk with them, so he hurriedly hid himself in the arbour.

They drew near. It was a still, pleasant evening. They sat down on one of the garden seats just in front of the place where Benedick was hidden. Then they called for Balthasar to come and sing for them.

Benedick listened as Balthasar played the melody on his lute.

"Is it not strange," he murmured to himself, "that sheep's guts should draw the souls out of men's bodies? Well, a horn for me any day."

So Balthasar began to sing:

> "Sigh no more, ladies, sigh no more,
>   Men were deceivers ever,
>   One foot in sea, and one on shore,
>   To one thing constant never,
>   Then sigh not so, but let them go,
>   And be you blithe and bonny,
>   Converting all your sounds of woe,
>   Into hey nonny nonny.
>
> "Sing no more ditties, sing no more,
>   Of dumps so dull and heavy,
>   The fraud of men was ever so,
>   Since summer first was leavy,
>   Then sigh not so, but let them go,
>   And be you blithe and bonny,
>   Converting all your sounds of woe,
>   Into hey nonny nonny."

When he had finished, the Prince praised him for his singing, which Benedick heard very impatiently. They dismissed the singer and began to talk, knowing well that they had a listener.

"What was it you told me to-day, Leonato," said Don Pedro with feigned surprise, "that your niece Beatrice was in love with Signior Benedick?"

" I never thought that lady would love any man," said Claudio.

" No, neither would I," said Leonato ; " but most wonderful that she should so dote on Signior Benedick, whom outwardly she has always seemed to abhor."

Benedick listened in amazement.

" Is it possible ? " he thought. " Does the wind sit in that corner ? "

" Indeed, my lord," Leonato went on, " I cannot tell what to think of it, but she certainly loves him with the most violent affection."

" Perhaps she is merely pretending," said the Prince.

" Yes, that is likely," echoed Claudio.

" Pretend ? " exclaimed Leonato. " There was never a pretence of love that came so near true love as hers."

" Why," said the Prince, " what are the signs of love she shows ? "

" What signs, my lord ? " said Leonato. " Why, she will sit——" He turned to Claudio, " You heard my daughter tell you how ? "

" She did indeed," said Claudio.

" How, I pray you ? " asked Don Pedro. " You amaze me. I would have thought her spirit invincible against the assaults of love."

" I would have sworn so too, my lord, and especially against Benedick," Leonato answered.

Benedick in his hiding-place was bewildered.

" I should think this a trick," he said to himself, " but that the old man said it."

" Has she made her affection known to Benedick ? " asked Don Pedro.

" No," said Leonato, " and says she never will, and that's her torment."

" This is so indeed," Claudio added, " so your daughter says. ' Shall I,' says she, ' that has so often treated him scornfully, write to him that I love him ? ' "

" This is what she says," Leonato continued, " when she begins to write to him ; for she will rise twenty times in the night, and there she will sit in her nightdress until she has covered a sheet of paper. My daughter tells me all. And then she tears the letter into a thousand pieces and blames herself that she should be so immodest to write to one that she knows will mock her."

Claudio added, " Then down upon her knees she falls, weeps, sobs, beats her heart, tears her hair, prays, curses, ' O sweet Benedick, God give me patience.' "

" She does indeed," said Leonato ; " my daughter says so ; and her feelings are so great that my daughter sometimes fears she will do something desperate to herself."

The Prince looked thoughtful.

" It were a good thing that Benedick should be told of it, if she will not tell it herself."

" What good would that do ? " said Claudio.

" He would make a jest of it and torment the poor lady worse."

" If he should," answered Don Pedro, " he deserves hanging.   She is an excellent lady."

" And she is exceeding wise," added Claudio.

" In everything," said Don Pedro, " except in loving Benedick."

In this way they went on talking about this strange love with mock seriousness as if they did not know what to do.   At last Don Pedro asked, " Shall we find Benedick and tell him of her love ? "

" Never tell him, my lord," Claudio replied. " Let her get over it by good advice."

" No, that's impossible," said Leonato.

" Well," said the Prince, " we will hear further of this from your daughter.   I love Benedick well, and I could wish that he could modestly examine himself and see how unworthy he is of so good a lady."

Enough had been said for the present.   They rose and walked towards the house.

When they were out of Benedick's hearing the Prince said, " Let the same trick be played on Beatrice.   But see that they meet.   Let us send Beatrice out to call Benedick in to dinner."

Benedick waited in his hiding-place until they had entered the house, then he came out into the open.

" This can be no trick," he said to himself ;

" their speech was serious. They have heard of this from Hero. They seem to pity the lady. Love her ? Why, it must be repaid. I hear how I am blamed ; they say I will bear myself proudly if I see she loves me, and that she will rather die than give me any sign of love. I never thought I should marry," he brooded. " I must not seem proud. Happy are they that hear themselves blamed and can mend." He began to have sweeter thoughts about love and marriage. " I will be horribly in love with her," he said. " I may have some jests made at me because I have railed so long against marriage, but does not the appetite alter ? A man loves the meat in his youth that he cannot endure in his age. No, the world must be peopled ; when I said I would die a bachelor I did not think that I should live until I were married."

Beatrice was coming down the path. He looked at her.

" She is a fair lady," he murmured ; " I spy some marks of love in her."

When she saw him she said in her usual way, " Against my will I am sent to bid you come in to dinner."

" Fair Beatrice," Benedick answered very gallantly, " I thank you for your trouble."

" I took no more trouble for those thanks than you take trouble to thank me. If it had been a trouble I would not have come."

" You take pleasure, then, in the message ? " said Benedick.

" Yes, just as much as you may take on a knife's point."

She turned and left him.

Benedick was happy. He saw a double meaning in her words.

" ' I took no more trouble for those thanks than you took trouble to thank me.' That's as much as to say, ' Any pains that I take for you is as easy as thanks.' Surely," he thought, " she is indeed in love with me."

He went off very happily, determined to buy her picture.

Hero was now ready to play her part in trapping Beatrice. She called her two gentlewomen, Margaret and Ursula, and told them what they must do. So Margaret went to tell Beatrice that they would be walking in the garden and talking about her. Hero and Ursula walked together down the garden path. Soon they spied Beatrice stealthily hiding herself. They therefore came by her hiding-place, and there began to talk of Benedick.

" But are you sure," said Ursula as if in astonishment, " that Benedick loves Beatrice so entirely ? "

" So says the Prince," Hero replied, " and my new lord."

" And did they bid you tell her of it, madam ? " asked Ursula.

" They begged me to tell her, but I persuaded them that if they loved Benedick they should wish him to wrestle with his affection and never let Beatrice know of it."

" Why did you so ? " asked Ursula.   " Surely the gentleman is well deserving ? "

" O God of Love ! " exclaimed Hero, " I know he deserves as much as any man, but Nature never made a woman of prouder heart than Beatrice.   She is full of disdain and scorn, and she values her own wit so highly that nothing can compare with it.   She cannot fall in love."

Ursula nodded agreement.

" I think so too," she said, " and therefore it were best that she did not know of his love lest she make sport of it."

" You speak truly," replied Hero, " I never yet saw a man, wise or noble, young or handsome, but Beatrice would mock him.   Therefore it is best that Benedick should rather wear himself away with sighing than die with Beatrice's mocking."

" Yet tell her of it," Ursula said ; " hear what she will say."

" No," answered Hero, " I would rather go to Benedick and tell him to fight against his love."

They sat talking thus for a little while, and then, still pretending that they had not noticed Beatrice, they went back to the house together. When Beatrice came out of her hiding-place her ears were burning with shame and astonishment ; and from this moment she began to fall in love with Benedick.

Don Pedro and Claudio were much excited to see what would happen next. They soon perceived that Benedick had been caught, for when he next appeared he was greatly changed. He had trimmed his beard neatly. His clothes were very fine. He had perfumed himself. He looked worried. The others recognized the symptoms and began to mock him. He made little reply, but walked away with Leonato.

Don John had now his opportunity. He came secretively to the Prince and Claudio and said that he wished to speak to them in private.

" What's the matter ? " asked the Prince.

" Does your lordship mean to be married to-morrow ? " he said to Claudio.

" You know he does," the Prince replied.

" I do not know that," said Don John, " when he knows what I know."

" If there is any impediment," said Claudio, " I pray you discover it."

" You may think that I love you not," said Don John in his shifty way ; " let that appear later."

" Why, what's the matter ? " asked the Prince.

" I have come to tell you," said Don John, " that the lady is disloyal."

" Who ?   Hero ? " cried Claudio.

"Yes," answered Don John, "even she, Leonato's Hero, your Hero, every man's Hero."

"Disloyal?" echoed Claudio.

"The word is too good to paint out her wickedness," said Don John. "Come with me to-night and you shall see her chamber window entered even on the night before her wedding. If you love her, then marry her to-morrow; but you will find it more honourable to change your mind."

"Can this be so?" whispered Claudio.

"I will not think it," said the Prince.

"If you will follow me," said Don John, "I will show you enough, and when you have seen more and heard more, act accordingly."

Claudio was much moved at these words, for he believed that Don John was speaking the truth.

"If I should see anything to-night why I should not marry her to-morrow in the congregation, where I should wed, there I will shame her."

"I will say no more about her," said Don John, "until you are my witnesses. Do nothing until midnight, and then you will see what happens."

When night came on the watchmen of the city assembled to do their duty. They were at the command of Dogberry the constable and Verges his assistant. Dogberry was a very ignorant man who loved to use long words of which he did not know the meaning, and he tried to impress his own importance upon the watch.

When they were all assembled and with their lanterns and weapons, he began to give them their instructions. He told them that they should arrest all vagrants and that they should bid any night walker stand in the Prince's name.

" What if he will not stand ? " asked one of the watch timidly.

" Why then, take no notice of him," said Dogberry. " Go and call the rest of the watch together, and thank God that you are rid of a knave."

" If he will not stand when he is bidden," added Verges, " he is not one of the Prince's subjects."

" True," added Dogberry, " and you are to meddle with none but the Prince's subjects. You shall also make no noise in the streets ; for, for the watch to babble and to talk is most tolerable and not to be endured."

" We would rather sleep than talk, we know the duties of a watch," answered one of the watchmen sagely.

" Why," said Dogberry admiringly, " you speak like an ancient and most quiet watchman ; for I do not see how sleeping could offend any one. Only have a care that your weapons are not stolen."

So Dogberry went on to tell them their duties, and he ended by commanding them that they should particularly watch round Signior Leonato's door, because the wedding being there in the morning, there was a great to-do this night.

At last, having seen that the watch knew their duties, Dogberry and Verges left them and went to bed.

The watch took up their places in the street. By and by Conrade and Borachio approached. Borachio had already earned his reward from Don John and spent some of it at the tavern, so that he was none too sober. He was eager to tell Conrade how his plan had worked. It was a dark night, and the rain was falling in a drizzle. They stood for shelter under an overhanging roof, where the watch heard everything they said.

" I have earned from Don John a thousand ducats," Borachio said.

His talk began to wander, and it was some time before Conrade could get out of him what great service had earned him such a sum. At last he said, " To-night I wooed Margaret, the Lady Hero's gentlewoman, calling her Hero. She leans out at her mistress's chamber window and bids me a thousand times good-night. I tell this tale vilely. I should first of all tell you of the Prince and Claudio and my master, who had been placed there to watch by my master Don John, who saw all this from the orchard."

" Did they think Margaret was Hero ? " asked Conrade.

" Two of them did, the Prince and Claudio, but

the devil my master knew she was Margaret;
and partly by his oaths, and partly by the dark
night, which deceived them, and partly by my
villainy it seemed to prove the slanders which
Don John had told them. Away went Claudio in
rage, and swearing that he will meet her the next
morning at the Temple, and there, before the
whole congregation, shame her with what he saw
to-night and send her home again without a
husband.''

At these words the watchmen came out from
their hiding-places and arrested both men. They
would listen to no protests, but marched them off
for the night to the lock-up.

Very early next morning Hero got out of bed
and began to dress for the wedding. Margaret
helped her to dress. By and by Beatrice came in.
She had not slept all night for thinking of Benedick. Margaret began to tease her. Beatrice
excused herself, but Margaret knew the cause of
her trouble and talked of Benedick mysteriously.

Then Ursula came in to say that the Prince,
the Count, and all the gallants had come to escort
her to church.

By this time the watch had told their tale to
Dogberry and Verges, who hurried along full of
importance to tell Leonato what they had found.
Leonato was very busy and had small patience to
listen to Dogberry's pompous words, for Dogberry
could never say a plain thing plainly.

"I must leave you," said Leonato impatiently.

"One word, sir," said Dogberry. "Our watch, sir, have indeed comprehended two aspicious persons, and we would have them this morning examined before your worship."

"Make the examination yourself," said Leonato irritably, "and bring it to me. I am now in great haste, as you can see."

"It shall suffice," Dogberry replied; for it would give him an opportunity of distinguishing himself.

Leonato went off to the church, leaving Dogberry and Verges to examine the prisoners.

When all were assembled in the church, Leonato called on the friar to begin.

"Be brief," he said, "only the plain form of marriage; you shall preach of their duties afterwards."

The bride and bridegroom stood before him, and he began the service.

"You come hither, my lord, to marry this lady?"

"No," replied Claudio.

"To be married to her," corrected Leonato. "Friar, you come to marry her," for Leonato did not understand what was happening and was somewhat agitated.

Then the friar said to Hero, "Lady, you come hither to be married to this Count?"

"I do," she said.

"If either of you know any impediment why

you should not be joined I charge you on your souls to utter it."

Claudio turned and looked at Hero.

" Do you know any, Hero ? " he asked.

" None, my lord," she answered.

" Do you know any, Count ? " the friar asked.

" I dare make his answer," Leonato said, " none."

" Oh, what men dare do ! " exclaimed Claudio. " What men may do ! What men daily do, not knowing what they do ! "

Then he thrust the friar aside and turned to Leonato.

" Father, by your leave, will you freely give me this maid, your daughter ? "

" As freely as God gave her me," replied Leonato.

" And what have I to give you back," said Claudio, " of equal worth to this rich and precious gift ? "

" Nothing," said the Prince, " unless you give her back again."

Claudio threw down her hand.

" There, Leonato," he cried, " take her back again. Would you not swear by her looks that she was an honourable lady ? But she is not ; she is an adulteress, and her blushes come from guilt, not modesty."

" What do you mean, my lord," cried Leonato in horror.

"Not to be married to a proved wanton," he replied. And he began to rage at her faithlessness so wildly that Hero asked if he was not well. Leonato asked the Prince why he did not speak.

"What should I speak?" said the Prince. "I am dishonoured, for I have tried to marry my dear friend to a common creature."

All were astonished at Claudio's action, and especially Leonato, Hero's father, for as yet Claudio had not explained why he had refused her. When Leonato questioned him, he replied, "Let me ask one question of your daughter, and bid her answer me truly."

"I charge you do so, as you are my daughter," said Leonato.

"What man," asked Claudio, "was he that talked with you last night out of your window between twelve and one? Now, if you are true, answer."

"I talked with no man at that hour, my lord," Hero replied.

"Then," said the Prince, "you are false. Leonato, I am sorry you must hear this; but on my honour, I myself and my brother and Count Claudio saw her, and heard her, at that hour last night at her chamber window talk with a ruffian, who has indeed confessed to be her lover."

When Hero heard this she fell in a faint on the floor.

Claudio walked out of the church, followed by the Prince and Don John. All the others followed, except Benedick, Beatrice, Leonato, and the friar. Beatrice knelt by her cousin. At last she opened her eyes. Leonato was in great distress, for he believed that what Claudio said was true. Only Beatrice indignantly defended the honour of Hero, though Benedick would not give judgment until he had probed the truth a little further.

" On my soul," cried Beatrice, " my cousin is falsely accused."

" Lady," inquired Benedick, " did you sleep with her last night ? "

" I have slept with her for the last year," answered Beatrice, " but not last night."

This seemed to Leonato sure proof that the accusation was true, and in his grief he wished that she might die. Then the friar spoke. He had been silent all this while watching Hero. In his eyes she did not behave like one with a guilty secret. He believed her to be innocent, and so he told Leonato.

" Friar, it cannot be," he answered ; " the only grace she has left is that she will not perjure herself by denying it."

" Lady," asked the friar, " who is the man you are accused of loving ? "

" They know who accuse me," Hero murmured. " I know none. My father, if you can prove that any man spoke to me at an unfit time, or that last night I spoke to any living creature, turn me away, hate me, torture me to death."

"There's some strange mistake in the Princes," said the friar.

"Two of them," Benedick remarked, "are very honourable : if they have been misled in this, it is a plot of Don John."

Leonato was now beginning to think more kindly of Hero, and his indignation against Hero's accusers increased.

"Pause awhile," the friar said, "and let me advise you. Your daughter here lay like dead when the Princes left her. Let her be hidden in secret, and give out that she is dead indeed. Put on mourning, and observe all the rites of a burial."

"What will this do ?" asked Leonato.

"This," the friar replied, "will make her slanderers pity her, and that is some good. Then it will happen that Claudio, when he hears that she is dead because of his cruel words, will begin to think sweetly of her. If he loves her at all, he will mourn for her and be sorry that he accused her. In time the truth will be known ; and even if it is not, the belief that she is dead will take away the slander from her, so that, if things do not turn out happily, you may conceal her in some convent away from men's eyes and tongues."

When he heard this Benedick also begged Leonato to take the friar's advice. Hero was too sad to say anything. She arose, and, taking the arm of her father and the friar, was led away into the house. Benedick and Beatrice were thus left alone for the first time since each supposed the other to be in love. Beatrice was weeping quietly for her cousin's misfortune. Benedick went up to her, " Lady Beatrice," he said, " have you wept all this time ? "

" Yes, and I will weep a while longer," she replied.

" I will not desire that," said Benedick.

" You have no reason, I do it freely," said Beatrice.

" Surely," said Benedick, " I do believe that your cousin is wronged."

" How much might the man deserve of me that would right her ! "

" Is there any way to show such friendship ? "

" A very straight way, but no such friend," said Beatrice.

" May a man do it ? "

" It is a man's office, but not yours."

Then Benedick began to speak out openly. He took Beatrice's hand and said, " I love nothing in the world so much as you. Is not that strange ? "

She looked up into his face.

" As strange as the thing I do not know," she answered in confusion. " If it were possible for me to say, I loved nothing so well as you . . . do not believe me . . . and yet I do not lie . . .

I confess nothing . . . I deny nothing ; I am sorry for my cousin."

But Benedick insisted until she confessed that she did indeed love him. Then, being in very happy mood, he wished that she would give him some command to prove his love.

" Come, bid me do anything for you," he cried.

She replied very bitterly, " Kill Claudio."

" Not for the wide world," Benedick exclaimed.

At this she would have broken away from him, but he would not let her go. At last he said, " Is Claudio your enemy ? "

Then Beatrice's indignation broke out, " Is he not proved a villain who has slandered, scorned, dishonoured my cousin ? If only I were a man ! What, pretend to be friendly with her until they come to be married, and then publicly accuse her ? O God, that I were a man ! I would eat his heart in the market-place ! "

Her bitterness was so violent that it was some time before Benedick could persuade her even to listen to him. At last he said, " Do you think in your very soul that Claudio has wronged Hero ? "

" Yes, as sure as I have a thought or a soul," she said.

" Enough," he replied ; " I have promised, I will challenge him."

He kissed her hand and left her.

By this time Dogberry was ready to examine the prisoners. He and Verges and the sexton

put on their gowns for so important an occasion.
Then the watch brought Conrade and Borachio
before them.

" What is your name, friend ? " said Dogberry.

" Borachio."

" Pray write down ' Borachio,' " he said to the
sexton.   " Yours, sir ? "

" I am a gentleman, sir, and my name is
Conrade."

" Write down ' Master Gentleman Conrade.'
Masters, do you serve God ? "

" Yes, sir, we hope," they both answered.

" Write down that ' they hope they serve God,'
and write ' God ' first ; but God forbid that God
should go before such villains.   Masters," he
continued, " it is proved already that you are
little better than false knaves.   How do you
answer for yourselves ? "

" Sir," replied Conrade, " we say we are none."

" A marvellous witty fellow, I assure you."
Then to Borachio, " Come you here, sir, a word
in your ear.   Sir, I say to you that it is thought
you are a false knave."

" Sir, I say to you we are none," Borachio
answered.

" Well, stand aside.   Before God, they are both
in a tale : have you written down, that ' they are
none ' ? "

The sexton was impatient of Dogberry's pom-
posity.

" Master Constable," he said, " you do not know the right way to go about an examination. You must call up the watch that are their accusers."

" Yes," agreed Dogberry, " that's the best way. Let the watch come forward. Masters, I charge you in the Prince's name, accuse these men."

One of the watchmen said, " This man said, sir, that Don John the Prince's brother was a villain."

" Write down," cried Dogberry in great indignation, " ' Don John is a villain.' Why, this is flat perjury to call a Prince's brother a villain."

" Master Constable——" Borachio began, but Dogberry interrupted him, saying, " I pray you, fellow, peace, I do not like your look, I promise you."

" What else did you hear him say ? " asked the sexton.

Another watchman replied, " Why, that he had received a thousand ducats of Don John for accusing the Lady Hero falsely."

" Flat burglary as ever was committed," exclaimed Dogberry.

" Yes, that it is," agreed Verges.

" What else, fellow ? " the sexton asked.

" That Count Claudio meant to disgrace Hero before the whole assembly, and not to marry her."

" What else ? "

" That's all."

" This is more, masters," said the sexton to the prisoners, " than you can deny. Prince John this morning has secretly stolen away. Hero was accused in this way, and with the grief of it has suddenly died. Master Constable, let these men be bound and brought to Leonato's. I will go before and show him the examination."

The sexton gathered up his papers and went out.

" Come," said Dogberry, "let them be bound."

Verges went over and laid his hands on Conrade.

" Off, coxcomb ! " cried Conrade, shaking himself loose.

" God's my life, where's the sexton ? " cried Dogberry. " Let him write down the ' Prince's officer coxcomb.' Come, bind them. You naughty varlet ! "

" Away ! " cried Conrade. " You are an ass ! You are an ass ! "

Dogberry boiled with indignation at this remark.

" Do you not suspect my place ? Do you not suspect my years ? Oh, that the sexton was here to write me down an ass ! But, masters, remember that I am an ass, though it is not written down. No, you villain ! I am a wise fellow. And what is more, an officer. And what is more, a householder. And what is more, as pretty a piece of flesh as any in Messina. And one that knows the law. And a rich fellow too. And one who has two gowns, and everything handsome about him. Bring him away. Oh, that I had been written down an ass ! "

Meanwhile the sorrows of Hero, and the dishonour brought upon his house by Claudio, were causing Leonato such grief that he almost died of it. His brother Antonio tried to comfort him, but he would listen to no comfort.

It so happened that as they were walking in the streets together, the Prince and Claudio passed by. They did not wish to speak to the old man and would have left them, but Leonato stood in their way. He began to threaten Claudio and to accuse him, and from that to challenge him. In this Antonio supported him, but the Prince would not allow Claudio to accept the challenge, and so left the old man.

Next they encountered Benedick. He greeted them very coldly.

" We almost had our noses snapped off by two old men without teeth," said Claudio.

" In a false quarrel there is no true valour," replied Benedick. " I came to seek you both."

Neither the Prince nor Claudio would take Benedick seriously, not even when he called Claudio a villain and challenged him to fight. Benedick endured their jesting, but at last he turned to the Prince and said, " My lord, I thank you for your many courtesies to me, but I must discontinue your company. Your brother Don John has fled from Messina. Among you, you have killed a sweet and innocent lady. As for my Lord Lackbeard there, he and I will meet, and until then peace be with him."

With these words Benedick left them.

" He is in earnest," said Don Pedro in amazement.

" In most profound earnest," Claudio answered, " and I'll warrant you for the love of Beatrice."

Then Dogberry, Verges, and the watch dragging their prisoners came by. Don Pedro at once suspected that his brother had again been up to some mischief, especially when he saw the watch with two of his brother's men. He asked Dogberry what offence they had committed.

" Sir," replied Dogberry, " they have committed false report ; moreover, they have spoken untruths ; secondarily, they are slanders ; sixth and lastly, they have belied a lady ; thirdly, they have verified unjust things ; and to conclude, they are lying knaves."

The Prince, who could make little of Dogberry's talk, then spoke to the prisoners themselves and asked them what they had done. Borachio, realizing that confession was his only defence, went down on his knees.

" Sweet Prince," he said, " do you hear me, and let this Count kill me. I have deceived even your very eyes. What your wisdom could not

discover, these shallow fools have brought to
light. In the night they overheard me confessing
to this man how Don John, your brother, bribed
me to slander the Lady Hero ; how you were
brought into the orchard, and saw me make love
to Margaret in Hero's clothes ; how you dis-
graced her when you should marry her. The lady
has died because of my and my master's false
accusation."

The Prince and Claudio were filled with horror
when they heard these words.

" Did my brother set you on to this ? " the
Prince asked.

" Yes," replied Borachio, " and paid me richly
for it."

Leonato and Antonio by this time had met the
sexton, who was coming with the examination of
the prisoners. They came to meet the watch, and
now joined the Prince and Claudio.

" Which is the villain ? Which of these is he ? "
asked Leonato.

Borachio confessed that he was the offender.

" Are you the slave," cried Leonato, " that has
killed my innocent child with your breath ? "

" Yes, I alone."

" No," said Leonato, looking at the Prince and
Claudio, " it is not so. Here stand a pair of
honourable men. The third is fled that had a
hand in it. I thank you, Princes, for my daughter's death. Record it with your high and

worthy deeds ; it was bravely done, when you think of it."

Claudio was very penitent at the old man's indignation.

"Choose your revenge yourself," he said. "Impose on me any penance you will, but yet my chief sin was in mistaking."

Leonato was somewhat mollified at his sorrow.

"I cannot bid you make my daughter live," he said ; "that is impossible. But I pray you both that you tell the people in Messina how innocently she died. Write an epitaph and lay it on her tomb, and sing it there in honour of the dead. And then, to-morrow morning, come to my house ; and since you could not marry my daughter, marry my niece. My brother has a daughter almost the copy of my child that is dead, and she is heir to both of us."

Claudio was overcome by this noble offer, and promised willingly.

"To-morrow, then, I expect your coming," said Leonato.

Then he spoke to Borachio, "This wicked man shall be brought face to face with Margaret, for I believe that she was in the plot."

"No," said Borachio, "she was not ; nor did she know what she did when she spoke to me."

"Moreover," said Dogberry, thrusting himself forward, "this plaintiff here, the offender, called me an ass. I beseech you let it be remembered in his punishment."

When Benedick went back to the house he called for Margaret and asked her to tell Beatrice that he had returned. He was now very much in love, and was attempting even to write verses in honour of his lady. But poetry was not for him.

Beatrice came out. She asked him what had happened between him and Claudio. He answered that Claudio must either take up his challenge or he would denounce him as a coward. This business being finished, he said, " Now tell me, for which of my bad parts did you first fall in love with me ? "

" For all of them together," Beatrice answered. " And for which of my good parts did you first suffer love for me ? "

" Suffer love ! " said Benedick. " A good phrase. I do suffer love indeed, for I love you against my will."

And so they sat talking in their old style, but with a new difference, until Ursula ran in to tell them that there was a great to-do in the house, for it was now proved that Hero had been falsely accused and that Don John was the author of all the mischief.

That night the Prince and Claudio paid their tribute at the tomb of Hero as they had promised.

Next morning all were assembled in Leonato's house for the coming of the Prince and Claudio.

Leonato prepared to carry out his little plot. He sent the ladies into another room and told them to mask their faces.

Then Leonato told the friar what he must do. At this Benedick spoke a word, " Friar," he said, " I must put you to some trouble."

" To do what, signior ? " asked the friar.

" To bind me, or undo me, one of them." Then he confessed to Leonato, " Truly, your niece regards me favourably. To-day I shall be joined in the state of marriage with her."

The Prince and Don Pedro were now at hand. They came in and greeted Leonato. Leonato called for his brother, who appeared with the ladies masked.

" Which is the lady I must take ? " asked Claudio.

" This is she, and I give her to you," said Antonio.

Claudio took the masked lady by the hand and begged her to reveal her face.

" No," said Leonato, " that you shall not, until you take her hand before this friar and swear to marry her."

" Give me your hand," said Claudio. " I am your husband if you will have me."

Hero removed her mask and replied, " And when I lived I was your other wife."

Claudio's heart was too full for words. He took her in his arms and kissed her.

" Stay a moment," said Benedick to the friar. " Which is Beatrice ? "

Beatrice came forward and took off her mask.

" Do you not love me ? " asked Benedick.

" Why, no more than reason," she answered.

" Why, then, your uncle, and the Prince, and Claudio have been deceived ; they swore you did."

" Do you not love me ? " asked Beatrice.

" In truth no, no more than reason," Benedick replied.

" Why, then, my cousin, Margaret and Ursula are much deceived, for they swore you did."

" They swore you were almost sick for me," said Benedick.

" They swore that you were almost dead for me," replied Beatrice.

They would have fallen again into their old wrangling had not Leonato stopped them.

" Come, come," exclaimed Leonato, " I am sure you love the gentleman."

" And I will swear to it," said Claudio, for he had found one of Benedick's poor poems ; and Beatrice, too, had been guilty of writing poetry, as Hero had found out. So Benedick had to confess that indeed he was in love.

" Come, I will have you," he said, " but I take you for pity."

" I would not deny you," Beatrice replied, " but yet I yield to great persuasions ; and partly to save your life, for I was told you were in a decline."

" Peace, I will stop your mouth," said Benedick.

So he took her in his arms and kissed her.

" How does Benedick the married man ? " mocked the Prince.

" I tell you, Prince," Benedick answered gaily, " a whole college of wits cannot mock me out of my good humour. Since I do intend to marry, I will take no offence at anything the world says against it, for man is a giddy thing."

Benedick called to them all to join hands and dance. The music was beginning when a messenger came in and went up to the Prince.

" My lord, your brother Don John has been arrested and brought back to Messina by armed men."

" Do not think about him until to-morrow," cried Benedick. " I will devise fine punishments for him. Strike up, pipers ! "

So they all joined hands and began to dance.

III

HAMLET, PRINCE OF DENMARK

HAMLET and Gertrude were King and Queen of Denmark. This King Hamlet was a famous warrior, well loved by his people and worshipped by his only son, who was also called Hamlet. It was the King's custom of a fine afternoon to sleep in his orchard. One day, when his servants came to wake him, they found him dead, and it was given out that a serpent had stung him. King Hamlet had scarcely been buried when Claudius, his brother, married Gertrude, and (since the throne of Denmark was filled by election) persuaded the Danes to choose him as their next king.

Not long after this there went a rumour amongst the sentinels who kept the guard over the palace at Elsinore that a strange figure was to be seen at midnight on the battlements. Some were frightened at this spectre ; others, who had not seen it, scoffed.

Two nights later the watch was kept by a

gentleman named Francisco. It was a cold, still night. As the time came for his relief he listened anxiously, eager to be gone. The clock struck midnight. Bernardo, the new sentry, appeared, and Francisco hurried away to his quarters.

Marcellus, Bernardo's partner, joined him. He had brought with him Horatio, a young Danish gentleman who was a scholar at the University of Wittenberg. Horatio had no faith in ghosts, and Marcellus easily persuaded him to take his place with the others for the night watch, so that if this apparition should chance to appear again he might speak to it.

The bell tolled one. Out of the darkness the ghost appeared. They gazed at it in fear and wonder. It was like the late King, very like. Horatio stepped forward and commanded it to speak, but it glided away without sound or word.

When it had gone, Bernardo asked Horatio whether this was not something more than imagination ; and with that they fell to talking of how like it was to the late King, and how twice before at this very hour it had appeared at this same place. Horatio replied that it was a sign that some strange danger threatened the State. This seemed very likely, for day and night the workmen were busy casting cannon and building ships, and working so hard that they did not rest even on a Sunday. The danger, said Horatio, was young Fortinbras, nephew of the old King of

Norway, who was collecting a band of desperate men to take back by force from Denmark certain lands which the late King Hamlet had won.

The ghost returned. When Horatio saw it, he rose from where he had been sitting and stood in its way. He commanded it—if it could speak—to speak to him. If there was any good thing that could be done to give it ease ; if it knew something of the State of Denmark ; if it had hidden treasure in the earth for which—it is said—spirits often walk after death. But before the ghost could make reply the cock crew, at which sign all ghostly things must return to their own confines. The ghost vanished as it had appeared.

The first light of dawn was now showing over the eastern hills. They agreed that when their watch was over they would go in and tell Prince Hamlet what they had seen.

That same morning Claudius, the new King of Denmark, held his first council. There were present with him Gertrude, his Queen, Polonius, the old Councillor of the Kingdom of Denmark, and his son Laertes, and others of the King's Council. Prince Hamlet kept apart and aloof from the rest, conspicuous among them in his black mourning.

The King began to speak. First he spoke of the death of his brother, and why he had married his brother's wife, the Queen. He thanked them all for supporting him. Next he spoke of young

Fortinbras and how he was demanding the return of those lands which the late King had won.

So Voltimand and Cornelius, who had been chosen as Ambassadors to the King of Norway, were summoned. Then the King delivered to them his message for the King of Norway, and the instructions laying down their duties.

When the Ambassadors had departed, the King next turned to Laertes, who had a request to make. He begged for leave to go back to France, whence he had come to take part in the King's Coronation. Polonius also supported this petition, which the King very willingly granted.

Then the King addressed words of sympathy to Hamlet who was heavy and downcast with his grief. He commended Hamlet for showing such love for his father, but, said he, to continue in such lamentation was displeasing to Heaven, a fault against Nature and reason. He begged him to lay aside this useless grief and think of him as his father, for he stood next to the throne. As for Hamlet's intention of returning to the University of Wittenberg, the King was not pleased. He asked him to remain at Court. When his mother also begged him, Hamlet agreed. The King was glad at this reply. He took Gertrude's arm and led her away. All the rest followed.

Hamlet was now alone. He began to lament very bitterly, and to wish either that he were dead or that God had not forbidden suicide.

Only two months had passed, not even two, since his father died; and yet his mother, who had followed his father's body to the grave all tears, had already married his father's brother.

While Hamlet was thus brooding over such thoughts, Horatio, Bernardo, and Marcellus found him. Hamlet greeted them eagerly, and especially Horatio.

He asked Horatio why he had come to Elsinore.

"My lord," he replied, "I came to see your father's funeral."

"Do not mock me," Hamlet answered bitterly. "I think it was to see my mother's wedding."

"Indeed, my lord," Horatio answered, "it followed soon after."

Then Horatio told Hamlet that he had seen his father only the night before.

"The King, my father?" asked Hamlet in amazement.

He begged Horatio to tell him what he had seen. So Horatio told how a figure like his father, all armed, with solemn step had passed by them three times while they kept the watch.

"I knew your father," Horatio said; "these hands are not more like."

Hamlet pressed them to tell him more, which they did very willingly. At last he agreed to keep watch with them that night.

"Perhaps," he said, "it will walk again."

"I warrant you it will" answered Horatio.

" If it appears like my beloved father," replied Hamlet, " I will speak to it, though Hell itself should bid me hold my peace."

So he told them both to say nothing of what they had seen, or what they might see ; and promised that he would be with them upon the battlements between eleven and twelve.

Meanwhile Laertes, having stowed his baggage on board ship, came to bid farewell to his sister Ophelia, for he had an important message to deliver to her. He had noticed that Hamlet was showing signs of love for her, and he wished to warn her not to think too much of his favours.

" Perhaps he loves you now," he said, " but yet his will is not his own. He may not, like other men, marry where he would. Then, if he says he loves you, remember that he may not do more than the State of Denmark allows. Be careful, therefore, dear sister, lest you give way to his desires."

They were still talking of this matter when Polonius, their father, came upon them.

Polonius was now growing old and verging on his dotage. When he saw Laertes, he urged him to hasten on board, but first he must bestow on him some wise advice on how a young man should behave himself in Paris ; which he did.

Laertes embraced his father, and then Ophelia, with the parting words, " Remember what I said to you."

As soon as Laertes had gone, Polonius asked what Laertes had said.

" Something concerning Prince Hamlet," she replied. This reminded Polonius what he himself had wanted to say.

" They tell me," he said, " that lately Hamlet has very often talked with you alone. If it is so, then I must warn you that you have not behaved as becomes my daughter. Tell me what is between you."

"My lord, he has made many offers of love to me."

" You speak like a green girl," said Polonius. " Do you believe his offers ? "

" I do not know, my lord, what I should think," she answered.

" I will teach you," he said. " Think yourself a baby."

" My lord," protested Ophelia, " he has made love to me in honourable fashion."

" Yes, I know," answered Polonius. " You must not take his words for true love. From this time forward do not be so free with yourself. As for Prince Hamlet, remember that he is young, and has more liberty than can be given to you. Do not believe his vows for they are false. And this for an end. In plain terms, from this time forth, I would not have you talk to Hamlet. Look to it, I tell you."

" I shall obey, my lord," meekly answered Ophelia.

Very late that night Hamlet joined Marcellus and Horatio on the battlements. From within the palace they heard the noise of trumpets and of the kettledrum and then the discharge of cannon.

" What does this mean, my lord ? " asked Horatio.

" The King makes feast to-night," Hamlet answered, " and as he drinks his toasts the kettledrum and the trumpet sound his pledge."

" Is it a custom ? " Horatio asked.

" Yes," said Hamlet, " but better dropped than observed."

Horatio turned.

" Look, my lord ! " he exclaimed ; " it comes ! "

When Hamlet saw the ghost, his mind was full of love for his dead father, and he cried out, " Hamlet, King, father ! " He begged it to answer him, and to say why the sepulchre had opened to send it forth again, to come back upon this earth armed like a warrior.

There was no sound, but the ghost beckoned to Hamlet to follow. Horatio and Marcellus were afraid and begged him to stay where he was, but Hamlet would not.

" Why should I fear ? " he said. " I do not value my life at a pin ; and as for my soul, what can it do to that ? I will follow it."

" What if it tempts you towards the sea, my lord ? Or the cliff ? And there assumes some horrible shape that may drive you mad ? " said Horatio.

Hamlet paid no attention. " Go on ! " he cried to the ghost ; " I will follow ! "

" You shall not go, my lord ! " cried Marcellus. They would have held him back by force, but Hamlet shook them off and followed, leaving Horatio and Marcellus uncertain what they should do ; but at length, as they were fearful for Hamlet's safety, they went after him.

After a while the ghost paused and beckoned, and began to speak : " Mark me. I am your father's spirit, doomed for a certain time to walk the night. Listen, Hamlet. If ever you loved your father, revenge his foul and most unnatural murder ! "

" Murder ? " echoed Hamlet.

" Murder, most foul and unnatural," said the ghost.

" Tell me quickly," answered Hamlet, " that as swift as thought or love I may sweep to my revenge."

" Now, Hamlet, hear," the ghost continued. " It was given out that, while I was sleeping in my orchard, a serpent stung me ; and this all Denmark believed. But know, the serpent that stung your father's life now wears his crown."

" My uncle ? " whispered Hamlet.

" Yes ; that adulterous beast with traitorous gifts won my Queen for himself. As I slept in my orchard your uncle stole upon me with a vial, and in my ear he poured his poison, so deadly that it raced through the blood as swift as quick-silver, curdling it like vinegar dropped in milk. Thus, as I slept, was I cut off by my brother's hand from life, from crown and queen, even with all my sins upon me, unrepented, and sent to my last account with all my imperfections on my head. If you are my true son do not endure it. But whatever you do, do nothing against your mother. Leave her to Heaven and to her conscience."

The morning was at hand, and as the first light appeared the ghost faded away.

Hamlet was filled with horror at this revelation, and when the others found him alone he spoke to them wildly. He would not tell them what he had seen or heard, only he made them swear by his sword that they would never speak a word of the events of the night, however strangely and oddly he should behave thereafter. Never, by nod, or hint, or suggestion, should they let it be known that they knew anything. They took this oath and then all three went in together.

Hamlet determined that he would test the truth of this strange revelation, for as yet he was still uncertain whether the spectre that he had seen was indeed his dead father, or some evil spirit sent to deceive him, or perhaps created by his own melancholy fancy.

He therefore pretended to have fallen into a melancholy madness, and in this state he wandered about the palace, brooding on his own thoughts. His feelings towards his uncle and his mother were as bitter as ever; and now Ophelia, too, seemed to have turned against him, for she would not speak with him or allow him to come to her.

At last he determined that he would seek her for himself. One day, as she was sewing in her chamber, he suddenly appeared before her, his doublet open, his stockings, dirtied and ungartered, hanging loose around his legs, and with a look of piteous sorrow in his face. He took her by the wrist and gazed in her face, saying nothing. At last, nodding his head, he uttered a piteous sigh. Then with his eyes fixed on her still, he turned and went out of the door. Ophelia was terrified and at once ran to tell her father. When Polonius heard, he was glad, for he thought that he had now discovered the cause of Hamlet's apparent madness.

" This is the very madness of love," he said. Then he began to ask her questions. " Have you given him any hard words lately? "

" No, my lord," Ophelia answered; " but as you commanded, I refused his letters, and would not allow him to come to me."

" That," said Polonius sagely, " has made him mad. I am sorry that I did not understand him better, for I thought he was trifling with you. Old folk as often are too careful in their judgments as the young are to lack discretion. Come, we will go to the King, for it must be made known."

When Polonius entered the King's chamber he found the King and the Queen consulting with Rosencrantz and Guildenstern. These two young men were of an age with Hamlet, and knew him well, for they had been brought up with him. The King had sent for them to beg them to amuse Hamlet and to gather from him—if they could—what was the cause of his melancholy.

Rosencrantz and Guildenstern very willingly promised that they would do what the King asked.

Polonius was very well pleased with himself. He had two pieces of news for the King : the first, that the Ambassadors from Norway had succeeded in their mission and were now returned ; and the second, that he had found the true cause of Hamlet's madness.

" Speak of that," said the King, " for I long to hear it."

" First," replied Polonius, " hear the Ambassadors."

So the King sent Polonius to bring them in. Then he told the Queen what Polonius had said, but she answered, " It is nothing else but the old cause ; his father's death and our hasty marriage."

When the Ambassadors came they told the King what had happened in Norway. The old King had found that his nephew did indeed propose to lead his army against the Danes ; but now he had sworn an oath that he would never attack Denmark ; instead, he would lead his army against the Poles. Further, he begged leave that he might be allowed to pass through Denmark on his way to the wars. The King thanked them for their good success, and dismissed them.

Polonius, being now alone with Claudius and Gertrude, began next to talk of Hamlet's madness. He was so excited with his discovery that it was a long time before he could come to the point. At last he said, " Listen. I have a daughter, that is, while she is my daughter, who dutifully and obediently has given me this. Now listen, and draw your own conclusions."

He took out a love letter which Ophelia had received from Hamlet and began to read it. Then he said, " This letter my daughter obediently showed me ; and more, she has told me everything that he said, when, and how, and where."

" But how did she receive his love ? " the King asked.

" What do you think of me ? " replied Polonius on his dignity.

" As a man," answered the King, " faithful and honourable."

" I would wish to prove myself so," replied
Polonius. " But what would you think, or what
would Her Majesty the Queen have thought, if I
had sat by dumbly, saying nothing ? No, I got
to work, and I spoke to my young mistress.
' Lord Hamlet,' I said, ' is not for you ; this must
not be.' Then I gave her orders that she should
lock herself away from him, allow no messengers,
receive no presents. That done, she took my
advice ; but Hamlet, to make a short tale of it,
being thus repulsed, first was sad, then fasted,
then grew weak, and so by degrees fell into the
madness in which he now raves."

" Do you think this is the cause ? " the King
asked Gertrude.

" It may be so," she answered. " Very likely."

" Has there ever been a time," Polonius asked
tartly, " when I have positively said it is so and
it has proved otherwise ? "

" Not that I know," answered the King.
" How may we test it ? "

" You know," said Polonius, " that sometimes
he walks here in the lobby four hours on end.
At such a time I will loose my daughter to him.
Then you and I behind the curtain will watch
what happens. If he does not love her, and if
that is not the reason for his madness, then I am
not fit to be a statesman."

While they were still talking, Hamlet wandered
towards them reading a book. Polonius bustled

the King and Queen out of the way, and then accosted Hamlet. Hamlet spoke to him strangely, and mocked the old man, who could make little of his answers, so that when Rosencrantz and Guildenstern appeared, he was glad to get away. Hamlet greeted his old acquaintances gladly; but yet he was somewhat suspicious of them, and began to question them. He asked them why they had come to Elsinore.

"To visit you, my lord," said Rosencrantz; "no other cause."

Hamlet thanked them. "But," he said, looking from one to the other, "were you not sent for? Is this your own desire? Come, tell me truly."

They hesitated.

"You were sent for," he cried. "There is a kind of confession in your looks which you are not crafty enough to conceal. I know the King and Queen have sent for you."

"But why, my lord?" asked Rosencrantz.

"That you must tell me," Hamlet answered; "but I beg you, by all that you hold dear, be straight and truthful with me, and tell me whether you were sent for or not."

Rosencrantz and Guildenstern looked at each other in some confusion, for they did not know what to answer. At last Rosencrantz said, "Yes, my lord, we were sent for."

"I will tell you why," Hamlet answered. "Of late, but why I do not know, I have lost all cheerfulness. Nothing pleases me. Neither man nor woman."

"Then, my lord," said Rosencrantz, "the Players will receive a poor welcome from you, for we met them on our way, and they are coming here to offer to play before you."

Hamlet was glad of this news, for he knew these Players of old, and they had proved a pleasant distraction.

Soon after the Players reached the castle.

Polonius ushered them into Hamlet's presence. He greeted them kindly, and he demanded that the chief Player forthwith should recite a speech to him. It was a speech of Æneas to Dido when he told her of the fall of Troy and the savage slaughter of old Priam, and the pitiful lamentations of his old wife Hecuba.

The Player came forward. He recited his speech with such eloquence and fervour that even Polonius was moved. When he had finished, Hamlet sent Polonius to find quarters for the Players, but as they were going out he called the chief Player to him.

"Can you play the 'Murder of Gonzago'?" he asked.

"Yes, my lord," said the Player.

"We will have it to-morrow night," Hamlet said. "You could, for the occasion, study a speech of a dozen or sixteen lines and insert it?"

"Yes, my lord," said the Player.

" Very well ; follow that old lord, and do not mock him."

When Hamlet was once more left alone he fell into a great passion. This Player, he thought, can be so moved by the mere imagination of his story that the tears start to his eyes. Yet what does he care for Hecuba ? What could he not do, had he the cause for passion that I have ? Yet I can say nothing, no, not even for a king so treacherously murdered. Am I a coward that I should endure any insult ? I must be ; or, before this, I should have given this treacherous villain as food for the kites.

Then suddenly there came into his mind the thought that sometimes a guilty person watching a play would be so moved that he would betray his guilt.

" I will make these Players play something like the murder of my father," he said to himself. " I will watch his looks. If he flinch, I shall know my duty. The spirit that I saw may have been the devil, for he has power to appear like a pleasing spirit ; and perhaps in my weakness and melancholy he seeks to draw me to destruction. I will have surer proofs than this. By this play I will entrap the conscience of the King."

When Rosencrantz and Guildenstern came back to Claudius and Gertrude they had to admit that they had failed to find out the cause of Hamlet's madness.

" He has confessed," Rosencrantz said, " that he feels himself disturbed, but he cannot be brought to speak of the cause."

" Nor do we find him eager to be questioned," added Guildenstern.

" Did you try to distract him with any amusements ? " asked the Queen.

Rosencrantz replied, " Madam, it so happened that we passed some Players on the road. When we told him of them, he seemed glad to hear it. They are already in the Court, and I think they have been ordered to play before him to-night."

" That is very true," Polonius remarked, " and he bade me ask your Majesties to hear this play."

The King heartily agreed, for he was glad to find something that could distract Hamlet.

It was now about the time when Hamlet was accustomed to pass the lobby in meditation. The King asked Gertrude and the others to leave him. Then Polonius gave Ophelia a book of prayers, and told her to appear to be reading it, so that Hamlet might come upon her thus employed. As Hamlet drew near, Polonius and the King hid behind the curtain.

At first Hamlet did not notice Ophelia. He was deep in thought, and his mind ran upon self-slaughter ; whether it was nobler to suffer all the mischances of this life, or to end them in an everlasting sleep. But, he thought, suppose that sleep were to be disturbed by dreams : this was the dread that made men endure all evil, lest by self-slaughter they should change a bad world for a worse. At length he noticed Ophelia seemingly deep in her devotions.

Ophelia greeted him timidly. Then she offered him those tokens which in former times he had sent her. At this Hamlet was moved to great anger, for it seemed to him that Ophelia too, like his mother, had revealed to him the corruption of mankind, and especially all womankind. He reviled her bitterly, and left her overcome with dismay.

The King and Polonius came out of their hiding-place.

" Love ? " said the King ; " he is not troubled with love. There is something on his mind, and I fear that when it comes to light it may be dangerous. We will send him to England to demand our tribute. Perhaps the sea and a new country will clear his mind. What do you think of it ? " he asked Polonius.

" It will do well," Polonius answered. " But yet," he went on reluctantly, " I do believe that the origin of his trouble sprang from neglected love."

Then he turned to Ophelia and said, " You need not tell us what Prince Hamlet said, we heard it all. My lord, do as you please, but if you think fit after the play let his Queen Mother all alone beg him to reveal his grief ; and, if it please you, I will be so placed that I can hear what passes. If she finds nothing, then send him to England."

" It shall be so," the King replied.

Evening came, and the time for the play. Hamlet sent for the Players and warned them to speak his speech as he would have it delivered, temperately, and without mouthing. Then he dismissed them to make themselves ready.

Next, before the Court appeared, he called for Horatio, who already knew of his suspicions of the King. Hamlet again confided in him, saying, " There is a play to be acted before the King to-night. One scene of it is very like the circumstances of my father's death. When you see it acted, watch my uncle closely. If his guilt does not reveal itself, then the ghost we have seen is an evil spirit and my imagination foul. But watch him carefully, as I will, and afterwards we will compare our judgments."

Claudius and Gertrude and all their courtiers came down into the hall and took their places for the play. Hamlet refused to sit by his mother, but lay on the ground at Ophelia's feet.

The play began.

First there was a dumb show, in which the actors mimed their play. A King and a Queen entered very lovingly. They embraced each other. The King lay down upon a bank of flowers. The Queen, seeing him asleep, left him.

After a while a man came in, took off the crown, kissed it, and poured poison in the King's ear. The Queen returned, found the King dead, and made sorrowful gestures. Some servants entered and carried the body away, but the poisoner made love to the Queen, wooing her with gifts. She seemed loath and unwilling for a while, but in the end she accepted his love.

All this was shown in their miming, but with such extravagant gestures that neither Claudius nor any of the others fully understood what it meant.

Then there came in a Prologue to ask for a patient hearing for their play. After him the King and Queen ; and the story which had been shown in mime was now repeated with words. The King told his wife that in a short time he would die, and then she must find another husband as kind as he. But she protested, saying :

> " In second husband let me be accurst,
>   None wed the second but who kill'd the first."

So the King went to sleep and the Queen left him.

" Madam," said Hamlet to his mother, " how do you like this play ? "

" The lady protests too much, I think," Gertrude answered uneasily.

" Oh," said he, " but she will keep her word."

Claudius was growing suspicious.

" Have you heard the story ? " he asked Hamlet. " Is there no offence in it ? "

" No, no," he muttered, " they do but jest. Poison in jest. No offence in the world."

" What do you call the play ? " asked the King.

" *The Mouse Trap*," said Hamlet. " This play is the story of a murder committed in Vienna. Gonzago is the Duke's name. His wife was Baptista. You shall see. It was a wicked piece of work. But what of that ? Your Majesty, and we that have free consciences, it does not touch us."

Another Player entered.

" This is Lucianus," explained Hamlet, " nephew of the King."

Lucianus crept nearer to the sleeping King. He bent over him and poured poison in his ear.

Hamlet was watching King Claudius closely.

" He poisons him in his garden for his estate," he said. " His name is Gonzago. You will see soon how the murderer gets the love of Gonzago's wife."

Claudius could endure it no longer. He rose and ran hurriedly from the hall.

In a moment all was confusion. The courtiers called for lights, and every one but Hamlet and Horatio hastily followed after the King.

Hamlet was very excited at this sudden end to the play. He and Horatio knew now for certain that the ghost had spoken truth and that Claudius was indeed the murderer of his father.

Soon Rosencrantz and Guildenstern came back.

Hamlet answered them wildly and contemptuously. They came to tell him that the Queen desired his presence immediately. Hamlet having fooled them a little further to make them think that he was indeed quite mad, at last promised that he would go straight to his mother. He was now ready and eager for his revenge.

When Rosencrantz and Guildenstern returned to the King, Claudius, who was both angry and frightened by what had happened, told them that he had determined straightway to send Hamlet to England and that they must go with him.

Polonius joined them.

"My lord," he said excitedly, "he is going to his mother's room. I will hide myself behind the curtains to hear what they say. I'll promise you she will speak to him straightly; and as you said, and very wisely too, it is right that some one besides his mother should overhear their speech. Farewell, my lord. I will call upon you before you go to bed and tell you what I know."

Claudius was now alone. He was overwhelmed by the sense of his crime, for it bore the curse of Cain, the first murderer, who also had murdered his brother. He would have prayed for forgiveness; but he could not pray from his heart, for how could he hope to be forgiven for the murder while he still held those things for which the murder was committed—the crown, and the Queen ? At last, in great agony of mind, he knelt, to force himself, if he could, to seek repentance.

As Claudius was thus kneeling, lost in his own thoughts, Hamlet passed by. At last, he felt, the time for his vengeance had come. He drew his sword and stealthily tiptoed towards the King, but when he saw that he was praying, he paused, as there came into his mind the words of the ghost. He remembered how his own father had been cut off without preparation or time for repentance, with all his sins upon his head. This was no moment for revenge, for if he should kill Claudius now, when his soul was in a state of grace, he would be doing him a kindness. He sheathed his sword, knowing that he must still wait until he could catch Claudius at some less holy time. He went on to his mother's chamber.

The King rose wearily from his knees, knowing nothing of the danger which had so nearly threatened him.

When Hamlet knocked at his mother's door, Polonius was already with her. He withdrew and hid himself. The Queen opened the door and Hamlet came in.

" Now, mother," he cried fiercely, " what's the matter ? "

" Hamlet," she replied, " you have greatly offended your father."

" Mother," he said, " you have greatly offended my father."

" Come, come," she said, " you answer me with an idle tongue."

" Go, go," he answered, " you question with an idle tongue."

The Queen was angry that Hamlet should treat her so rudely and she rose. Hamlet took her by the hand and forced her to sit down.

" You do not go," he said, " until I show you yourself as you are."

The Queen was frightened at these words, for she thought that Hamlet would murder her. She called for help, and Polonius too, from his place behind the curtains, began to cry out. Hamlet had not understood that he was being overheard. He thought it was the King. He drew his rapier and thrust it through the curtains at the figure which moved behind.

" Oh ! what have you done ? " cried the Queen.

" I do not know," he answered. " Is it the King ? "

He drew back the curtains, and there was Polonius dead on the floor.

The Queen was lamenting and wringing her hands. Hamlet spoke to her fiercely.

" What have I done," she cried, " that you dare speak so rudely to me ? "

Hamlet came beside her and took from his

breast the picture of his father that he always wore. Gertrude also was wearing a little picture of Claudius. Hamlet set the two pictures together. He pointed to that of his father.

"Look at this picture," he said, "and this, the portraits of two brothers. See what a man this was; how graceful, like Jupiter himself, or Mars. A man indeed that every god had graced. This was your husband. Look now what follows." Then, pointing to the other picture, he went on, "Here is your husband, like a mildewed ear corrupting the other. Have you eyes? Could you love this for this? You cannot call it love, for you are too old to fall in love without reason; and by what reason could you go from this to this?"

He spoke so fiercely to her that she was overcome with remorse and begged him to cease. Suddenly it seemed to Hamlet that the ghost of his father was standing before him, speaking to him and urging him not to forget his purpose of revenge. Gertrude saw nothing, but supposed that it was yet another sign of Hamlet's madness.

"Madness?" he cried. "My pulse beats as evenly as yours. It is not madness that I have uttered. Mother, for love of grace, do not flatter yourself that it is not your sin but my madness which speaks." And he went on again to rebuke her for her marriage with his uncle. At last he grew calmer. He said good-night to his mother, and then, taking the body of Polonius by the two legs, he dragged it out of her bedroom.

The King waited long for Polonius to come to him, but at last, fearing that something must have happened, he went to the Queen's chamber. There he found her weeping and wringing her hands.

" What is the matter, Gertrude ? " he asked. " Where is Hamlet ? "

" Mad as the sea," she moaned. " In his lunacy, hearing something stir behind the curtain, he drew his rapier and killed the old man."

" That," replied the King, " would have been my fate if I had been there. His liberty is dangerous to us all ; to you, to me, to every one. This deed will be blamed on us, for we should have kept this mad young man restrained. Where has he gone ? "

The King called for Rosencrantz and Guildenstern.

" Go, both of you," he said. " Hamlet, in his madness, has slain Polonius, and has dragged the body away. Find out where he is, speak gently to him, and bring the body into the chapel."

They straightway went in search of Hamlet, and at last they found him. He would not tell them where the body was, but answered them wildly and madly.

This deed of Hamlet's greatly disturbed the King, for though he would gladly have put

Hamlet to death, he dared not, because of the love which the people bore him. He determined therefore to have Hamlet murdered.

Rosencrantz and Guildenstern returned, leading Hamlet with them; but still he would not tell where they could find the body of Polonius, and when the King questioned him he replied, "At supper."

"At supper? Where?" asked the King.

"Not where he eats, but where he is eaten." Hamlet answered. "The worms are at him now."

"Where is Polonius?" the King asked again.

"In heaven," said Hamlet. "Send some one to see. If the messenger does not find him there, look in the other place yourself. But indeed, if you do not find him by the end of this month, you will smell him as you go upstairs into the lobby."

"Go," said the King to Rosencrantz and Guildenstern, "look for him there."

"He will wait until you come," jeered Hamlet.

The King, for all his anger, spoke softly to Hamlet, saying, "Hamlet, for your own safety we must send you quickly out of the country. Therefore prepare yourself. The ship is ready; everything is ready for you to go to England."

So Hamlet went off to make his preparations. The King by this time had made further plans; he would so devise it that Rosencrantz and Guildenstern should escort Hamlet to England, but they should carry with them letters commanding that he should be put to death immediately.

Next day they set off towards the harbour. On the way they passed a large troop of soldiers. They were some of the army of Fortinbras, and Fortinbras himself was with them on their way to fight against the Poles. Hamlet asked one of the soldiers the cause of their war.

" Truly," said the soldier, " we fight for a little patch of ground that is worth nothing but the honour of winning it. I wouldn't rent it for five ducats, and it is worth no more to Norway or to Poland."

" Why, then," said Hamlet, " the Poles will never defend it."

" Yes," said the captain, " it is already garrisoned."

This put Hamlet once more in mind of his own troubles. For all his talking, he had not yet revenged the death of his father, though he had cause and strength to do it. Yet this army was risking all for a thing that was not worth an eggshell.

So Hamlet went on board, and the ship put out to sea.

After a time, when Ophelia learnt that her father was dead and Hamlet had gone from the Court, she was so greatly distressed that she became quite mad. She wandered about the

Court speaking of her father in broken speeches, and in such a strange way that all who heard her suspected much. She would sing, too, very sweetly and pathetically.

The King was much disturbed by all these events ; first the death of Polonius, then Ophelia's madness, but besides all this he knew that the people were whispering against him. Moreover, Laertes had heard rumours in Paris and had come back hastily to Denmark, where in secret he waited his chance of revenging the death of his father. In a few days he had gathered a party of discontented men, and at their head he suddenly broke into the palace and into the very presence of the King himself.

" Oh, you vile King ! " he cried, " give me my father ! "

Claudius was no coward. He answered Laertes boldly.

" Tell me," he said, " why you are so enraged ? "

" Where is my father ? " cried Laertes.

" Dead," said the King.

" But not by him," added Gertrude.

" Let him ask what he will," replied the King.

" How came he dead ? " demanded Laertes. But the more he raged, the more quietly Claudius answered him, declaring that he was not guilty of Polonius's death, but grieved for it greatly, as he would prove.

While they were thus in talk, Ophelia herself wandered in.

She did not know her brother, but in her madness she thought that she was carrying a basket of herbs, and she went round to them giving to each in turn that herb which in the language of flowers seemed most fitting. To Laertes, rosemary and pansies, for they signified remembrance and thoughts ; to the Queen she gave fennel and columbine, which stood for flattery and thanklessness ; and to the King she gave rue and a daisy, for they stand for repentance and false show.

" I would have given you some violets," she murmured (for they signified faithfulness), " but they all withered when my father died." And so saying she wandered away again singing.

Laertes broke into weeping at this sad sight. When the King saw it, he said, " Come with me ; choose any friends you will, and they shall hear and judge between us. If directly or indirectly they find me guilty of the death of your father, I will give you all I possess to satisfy you—my kingdom, my crown, and my life. But if not, then you must patiently listen to me and we must work together for revenge."

Horatio was still about the Court. One of the servants came to him with a message that there was a sailor with letters wishing to see him. Horatio sent for the sailor. When he came he gave him a letter from Hamlet. Horatio opened it and read. It was a message from Hamlet that after two days at sea the ship had been overtaken by pirates. When the two ships came together Hamlet had leaped on board the pirate ship, but at that instant they got clear of his ship and so he became their prisoner, but they had brought him back to Denmark and released him.

" Let the King have the letters I have sent," the message went on, " and come to me as quickly as you fly death. I have words to whisper in your ear, which will make you dumb. These sailors will bring you where I am. Rosencrantz and Guildenstern go on to England. Of them I have much to tell you."

Horatio went off to find the King, who by this time had told Laertes the story of how Hamlet, and not he, was guilty of Polonius's death.

" Tell me then," asked Laertes, " why you took no action against him for this crime ? "

" For two reasons especially," the King replied, " though they may not appear to you very strong. The Queen almost lives for him ; and as for me, she is so dear to my life that I cannot do anything that will hurt her. The other reason why I cannot bring him to a public trial is the great love that the people bear him."

" So then," Laertes said bitterly, " my father is dead, and my sister driven into madness. But my revenge will come."

" Do not sleep less soundly for that," the King

replied. " You will hear more shortly. I loved your father, and I love myself."

At this moment the messenger entered with letters from Hamlet for the King and for the Queen.

" From Hamlet ? " said the King in astonishment. " Who brought them ? "

" Sailors, my lord, they say."

The King dismissed the messenger. Then he opened the letter and began to read it to Laertes. It was short, and said in a few words that Hamlet had returned to the kingdom, and on the next day begged leave to see the King, when he would tell him the reason for his sudden and strange return.

The King was astonished. " What should this mean ? " he asked. " Are all the rest come back ? Or is it some trick ? "

" Do you know the hand ? " Laertes asked.

" It is Hamlet's writing," said the King.

" Let him come," cried Laertes eagerly, " then I shall tell him face to face, ' This you did.' "

" If it should be so, Laertes," said the King smoothly, " will you be guided by me ? "

" So long as you do not persuade me to be peaceful."

" If he has now returned," Claudius went on, " because he will not go on this voyage, I will persuade him to an action which will bring about his downfall, and in such a way that no one can blame us for his death. Even his mother will think it an accident."

" My lord," said Laertes, " I will do what you ask if you can so bring it about that I may be the instrument of Hamlet's death."

Claudius answered, " You have been much talked of since you went abroad, and sometimes in Hamlet's hearing, for a quality which he especially envied."

" What was that, my lord ? " asked Laertes.

" Two months ago there came to our Court a gentleman from Normandy. I have myself seen and served against the French, and they do well on horseback ; but this gallant seemed to have some magic in him, for he rode his horse as if he had been part of the beast. He spoke of you, and highly praised your skill at fencing, especially with a rapier. This report of his so roused Hamlet's envy that he would do nothing but beg that you might be sent for to fence with him. Now," said the King, " out of all this . . . ."

He paused.

" What out of this ? " asked Laertes.

" Laertes," at last the King said, " was your father dear to you ? Or do you pretend to feel sorrow ? "

" Why do you ask ? "

" Not because I do not think you did not love your father, but because time changes everything. Hamlet comes back. What would you undertake to show that you are your father's son in deeds as well as words ? ''

" To cut his throat in the church ! '' cried Laertes.

" Good Laertes,'' Claudius said, " will you do this ? Keep to yourself. When Hamlet comes back he shall be told that you have come home. We will persuade some of our courtiers to praise your skill in his hearing. This will bring you together and we will wager on the fight. Hamlet will be careless, for he is of an open nature, and will not examine the foils ; and then easily, or with a little shuffling, you may choose a sword unblunted, and, as it were by accident, run him through.''

" I will do it,'' replied Laertes exultantly. " I have a poison which I bought, so deadly that if a man is but scratched with it, he will die. I will anoint my point, and with this, if I just touch him, it will be death.''

The King paused and considered. Then he said, " We must have some second course if this should fail. Let me see. I have it. During your contest, when you are hot and thirsty—and make your fencing more violent for that purpose—he will call for drink. I will have prepared for him a cup ; if he sip it, and by chance escape your poisoned sword, then he may be caught that way.''

This plot greatly pleased Laertes, but his

thoughts were soon distracted, for the Queen
came in weeping bitterly.

" Your sister is drowned, Laertes," she cried.

" Drowned ? " he answered. " Where ? "

So the Queen told the story as she had heard it.
Ophelia had gone down to the brook, her arms
full of wild flowers. There she had clambered on
to an old and rotten willow which threw a branch
across the stream. It broke beneath her, and
down she fell into the water. For a while her
clothes bore her up as she floated there singing ;
but not for long.

Next day the gravedigger set about digging a
grave for Ophelia. He was at his work when
Hamlet and Horatio, on their way back to the
palace, passed by. The gravedigger was singing
as he dug. Hamlet paused.

" Does this fellow," he said, " think so lightly
of his work that he sings while making a grave ? "

So they stood on the edge of the grave and
watched him. The gravedigger threw up a skull
and clapped it on the earth. Then he dug out
some bones and threw them up too. Hamlet
looked at the skull and began to brood over it.
He asked the gravedigger whose it was.

" That ? " said the man ; " he was a mad
fellow. Whose do you think it was ? "

" I do not know," said Hamlet.

" Why," said he, " that skull, sir, that skull
was Yorick's skull, the King's jester."

" This ? " said Hamlet in horror.

" Even that," said the man.

" Let me see it," Hamlet replied, picking up the skull. " Poor Yorick. I knew him, Horatio. He carried me on his back a thousand times. Here hung the lips that I have kissed I know not how often. Where are your songs now, and your jokes ? Now go to my lady's chamber and tell her, though she paints an inch thick, this is what she will look like. Make her laugh at that."

Then they saw the funeral approaching. So they stepped back, and hid themselves behind the tombs. First came the bearers with the corpse, then the King and Queen, with Laertes following. Last of all came a priest. Hamlet was astonished, for he did not know, as yet, who the dead was ; but he saw from the scanty ceremony that the dead had done some violence to itself. Laertes spoke to the priest, asking whether this was all the honour they could show to the dead. The priest replied unkindly : " We should profane the service of the dead if we sing a solemn requiem over her as to those who die in peace."

" Lay her in the earth," cried Laertes, " and from her fair flesh may violets spring. I tell you, churlish priest, my sister will be a ministering angel when you lie howling."

So Hamlet knew that this must be Ophelia. Laertes stood by the open grave, and then, so frantic was his grief, he jumped in, that he might once more take Ophelia in his arms. Hamlet stepped forward and jumped down into the grave by the side of Laertes. At the sight of him Laertes's rage broke out. He gripped Hamlet by the throat, and they began to fight and struggle in the open grave until they were parted. Hamlet was amazed at this outburst, for he did not know why Laertes should show such bitter hatred.

He wandered away sadly with Horatio. Then he told him how he had escaped from Rosencrantz and Guildenstern. One night he could not sleep. So he rose from his cabin, put on his sea gown, and crept in the darkness to the cabin of Rosencrantz and Guildenstern. He entered it, and there found the letter which they were carrying to England. He took it back to his own cabin and unsealed it. There he read the King's message, that straightway on the reading, without a moment's respite, his head should be cut off. He thought quickly. He sat down, wrote out a new letter, earnestly begging the English King that immediately he read it, without any delay, he would have the bearers put to death. As it chanced, he had his father's signet with him, which was like the other seal. He folded the letter like the first, sealed it, and placed it safely in Rosencrantz's cabin. The next day was the sea fight, and so Hamlet had escaped, whilst Rosencrantz and Guildenstern went unsuspecting to their deaths.

That same evening the King sent Osric, a very

fantastical and foolish courtier, to bear his message to Hamlet that he had wagered against Laertes six Barbary horses against six French rapiers and daggers, that in a dozen passes between Hamlet and Laertes, Laertes would not score more than three hits over Hamlet. If Hamlet would come to the trial it would please the King. Hamlet consented.

So all the Court came down into the hall to watch this contest, which was to be with rapier and dagger. The King called to Hamlet and to Laertes and made them shake hands. Hamlet asked his pardon, and though he did not know what the offence might be, yet he excused it as due to his madness ; it was nothing intended. Laertes took his hand. Hamlet called for the foils and each chose one. They stripped off their doublets ready for combat, and stood facing each other.

The King called for cups of wine, and commanded that if Hamlet should gain the first, the second, or the third bout, all the cannon on the battlements should fire as he pledged Hamlet's health. Moreover, he would drop into the cup, as a reward for Hamlet, a pearl of great value. He called for them to begin.

They played the first round, and after a while Hamlet touched Laertes.

They played the second round, and again Hamlet touched Laertes.

The King called for them to rest. He took the cup and dropped in it the pearl, but only he knew that the pearl was poisoned. Then he sent the cup to Hamlet, and at the same time the drums and trumpets sounded and the cannon were fired. Hamlet would not drink, but ordered the cup to be put aside for a while.

So they played the third bout, and again Laertes was touched.

The Queen was so pleased by this prowess of Hamlet that, to the King's horror, she took up the poisoned cup and pledged his health, but Claudius dared not stop her. Still Hamlet would not drink.

Laertes by this time was growing desperate, and he assailed Hamlet so fiercely that he drew blood. Hamlet thus knew that Laertes was fighting with an unblunted rapier. He returned to the attack, and grasping Laertes by the wrist wrung from him his rapier, dropping his own in exchange. Then he pressed Laertes and again touched him, but this time with the poisoned rapier, which drew blood.

Hamlet was now keyed up for the fight and cried to Laertes to come again, but the poison was already working. The Queen swayed and fell. Laertes too knew himself to be mortally wounded. As the Queen fell, she cried out, " The drink ! The drink, my dear Hamlet, the drink ! The drink ! I am poisoned ! " And with these words she was dead.

Hamlet called to the courtiers to lock the doors whilst they sought for the traitor.

" He is here, Hamlet," said Laertes. " Hamlet, you are slain ; no medicine in the world can do you good. You have not half an hour to live. The treacherous instrument is in your own hand unblunted and poisoned. Your mother's poisoned —the King's to blame."

Claudius was already trying to slip away, but Hamlet caught hold of him and stabbed him with the poisoned rapier ; and, to make sure, he took up the half-empty cup of poison and forced it between his lips. So at last Claudius was repaid for his crimes ; but soon Hamlet felt the poison creeping over him.

" I am dead, Horatio ! " he said. " You live. Speak truly of me and tell my tale."

" Do not believe it," Horatio answered. " I am more of an ancient Roman than a Dane, there is yet some poison left."

But Hamlet sprang at him and tore the cup from his hands.

" Let go ! " he cried. " Dear Horatio, if ever you loved me, live on to tell my tale."

From far away could be heard the sound of a drum and the cannon firing a salute.

" What noise is that ? " asked Hamlet. It was Fortinbras on his way back from Poland saluting the Ambassadors who had come from England.

Hamlet was now near death. " I cannot live,"

he murmured, " to hear the news from England, but I prophesy that Fortinbras will be chosen. He has my dying voice. So tell him. The rest is silence."

And these were the last words that he spoke.

IV

KING LEAR

Long ago, long before even the Romans came, the Kingdom of Britain was ruled by an old king called Lear. He was a tyrannical old man, and no one had dared to thwart him for so many years that he had grown used to having his own way in everything. Thus it came about that though he was now growing near his dotage, he still thought that every one should give way to his whims and fancies.

King Lear had three daughters; Goneril the eldest, Regan, and Cordelia, who was the youngest, and his favourite child. Goneril was married to the Duke of Cornwall, Regan to the Duke of Albany, but Cordelia was, as yet, unmarried, though at this time both the King of France and the Duke of Burgundy were sojourning in Lear's Court, each as a suitor for Cordelia.

Now it happened that Lear took it into his head to resign his throne. He determined to divide his kingdom amongst his three daughters, and to spend the last days of his life cared for by Cordelia. He therefore summoned his Council, and ordered the map of Britain to be laid before him. Thereupon he traced out the divisions into which the kingdom was to be divided, and assembled his whole Court that he might publicly announce his determination.

Lear wished this event to be very memorable, and knowing that he had given Cordelia the largest share, he wished also for some excuse for favouring his youngest daughter.

The Court therefore assembled. First came one carrying a coronet ; then Lear ; then the Dukes of Albany and Cornwall ; after them Lear's three daughters, followed by the rest of the lords, ladies, and courtiers, amongst whom were the Earls of Kent and Gloucester.

Lear sent Gloucester to summon the King of France and the Duke of Burgundy. He seated himself on his throne, and when all the others had taken their places, he called for the map and began to speak.

" Know," he declared, " that we have divided our kingdom into three, and it is our firm intention to leave all care and business to younger strength. It is our will to publish our daughters' dowers, that future strife may be prevented now. Tell me, my daughters, which of you shall we say loves us most, that we may bestow our bounty where it is most merited. Goneril, our eldest born, speak first."

Goneril had no love for the old man, but she was ready witted, and quickly framed an answer that would please him. She stood forth and said, " Sir, I love you more than words can say ; better than eyesight and liberty ; beyond what can be valued ; no less than life, grace, health, beauty, honour ; as much as any child ever loved her father. It is a love that cannot be uttered ; all this and more, I love you."

When Cordelia heard these words she was downcast and frightened, for she knew that she would never be able to express her love for her father.

So Lear unrolled the map and pointed to that part of the kingdom which he had already determined to assign to Goneril. It was a rich land, with forests and meadows, and full flowing rivers. So Goneril went back to her husband Albany well satisfied with the success of her speech.

Then Lear turned to Regan.

" What does our second daughter say," he asked, " our dearest Regan, wife of Cornwall ? "

Regan echoed the words of Goneril.

" I am made like my sister," she said ; " value me with her. Truly, I find that she exactly names my love except that she is too modest. I declare that I hate all other joys, and am only happy in your Highness's love."

When Cordelia heard these words she was more frightened than ever, for she knew that she could never frame her tongue to utter the like.

So Lear again took the map and showed those lands which he had reserved for Regan, as wide and fertile as Goneril's portion.

Regan stepped back to Cornwall, and Cordelia came forward.

Lear looked at her lovingly, expecting from her the kindest flattery of all.

" Now, our joy ! " he said, " although our last, and least, what can you say to warrant a third far richer than your sisters' ?   Speak."

But Cordelia could not utter a word.   At last she said, " Nothing, my lord."

" Nothing ? " echoed Lear.

" Nothing."

Lear's temper was beginning to rise at this unexpected rebuff.

" Nothing will come of nothing," he said sternly. " Speak again."

Cordelia in her misery answered, " Alas, I cannot heave my heart into my mouth ; I love your Majesty as it is my duty ; no more, no less."

" How, Cordelia ? " answered Lear.   " Mend your speech a little, lest you mar your fortune."

Cordelia, more wretchedly than ever, cried out :

" My good lord, you are my father ; you have bred me and loved me.   I obey you, love you, and honour you as I should."   And then, knowing that this but made matters worse, she said, " Why have my sisters husbands, if they say all their love is for you ? When I shall wed, my lord would take half my love with him. I shall never marry like my sisters, and still keep all my love for my father."

" But is this what your heart feels ? " asked Lear.

" Yes, my good lord."

" So young and so untender ? "

" So young, my lord," she answered, " and true."

Then Lear's rage broke out.

" Then let it be so ! " he shouted. " Truth shall be your dowry ! By the sacred warmth of the sun, I here cease to be your father, and henceforth hold you as a stranger to me for ever ! "

So fiercely did Lear begin to rage that the Earl of Kent stepped forward to plead for Cordelia, for he knew that the old King was grievously mistaken. But Lear cried him down.

" I loved her most," he said, " and thought that she would have cared for me." And he shouted, " Let France and Burgundy be summoned ! "

So blind was his wrath that he determined without further thought that Cordelia should have nothing, and that her share should be divided at once between Cornwall and Albany ; and this he immediately decreed, investing these two dukes with all his power, but with this one condition, that a following of one hundred knights should be reserved for him, and, with these to attend him, he would live with Goneril and Regan, with each a month in turn ; and further, that he should retain the name and noble title of a King. The rest, the power, the revenues, he delivered to his sons-in-law.

Once again Kent tried to prevent Lear from committing an act of such folly. He went on his knees before the King and begged to be heard ; but still Lear would not listen. Then Kent, in spite of Lear's threats, cried out to him :

" I will forget my manners when my King is mad ! It is my duty to speak plainly when my King listens to flattery. Keep your power ; think again before you commit this hideous rashness ! Your Highness's youngest daughter does not love you least."

" Kent," shouted the King, " on your life, no more ! "

But the more Lear raged, the louder Kent answered him. At last Lear made him listen, on his allegiance as a true subject. Then he pronounced this doom :

" Since you have sought to make us break our vow, which we never durst yet, and since you have tried to come between our decree—and this we cannot endure—take your reward. We allot you five days to provide for yourself. On the sixth, turn your back upon our kingdom. If, on the tenth day, you are found in our dominions, you die." And he swore by a solemn oath that this should be so.

Kent, knowing that nothing would turn the old man from his folly, sadly made his way out of the Court.

By this time Gloucester had returned with France and Burgundy. Lear spoke first to Burgundy.

" My Lord of Burgundy," he said, " what is the least that you will ask as dowry with our daughter ? "

" Most royal Majesty," Burgundy answered, " I ask no more than your Highness offered."

" When we loved her," Lear answered, " we held her valuable, but now her price has fallen. There she stands. If you care for her as she is, and with no dowry except our displeasure, she is there, and she is yours."

Burgundy was astonished at this change.

" I cannot answer," he said.

" Will you take her ? Or leave her ? " asked Lear.

Burgundy replied, " Pardon me, sir, I cannot choose on such conditions."

" Then leave her," said Lear, " for I have told you all she possesses."

Then he said to France :

" For you, great King, I would not have you marry one whom I hate. Therefore I beseech

you turn your love towards one worthier than a
wretch that Nature is almost ashamed to acknow-
ledge."

" This is most strange," replied France, " but
now she was your best of daughters. Surely in
this short time she must have committed some
monstrous action, or else your love must have
changed, which I will never believe."

Then Cordelia, who all this while had stayed
silent and downcast, cried out, " Yet I beseech
your Majesty—although I have not a glib tongue
to speak what I do not intend—that you make
known that it is no murder, or foulness, or
unchaste action, or dishonourable deed that has
deprived me of your grace and favour ; but only
the lack of that for which I am richer—a greedy
eye and such a tongue that I am glad I have not."

" You had better not have been born," Lear
answered, " than not to have pleased me better."

" Is it nothing but this ? " said France. " A
slowness in speech which leaves unsaid what it
intends to do ? My Lord of Burgundy, what do
you say to the lady ? Love is not love when it
needs rewards. Will you have her ? "

" Royal King," said Burgundy to·Lear, " only
give that dowry which you yourself proposed,
and I will take Cordelia by the hand to make her
Duchess of Burgundy."

" Nothing ! " cried Lear. " I have sworn. I
am firm ! "

" I am sorry, then," said Burgundy to Cordelia, " as you have lost your father, so you must lose a husband."

" Peace be with Burgundy," answered Cordelia mockingly, " since good name and dowry are what he loves. I shall not be his wife."

But France replied, " Fairest Cordelia, most rich when poor, most choice when forsaken, you and your virtues I choose. Your dowerless daughter, King, becomes my Queen. Not all the Dukes of Burgundy can buy this precious maid from me."

" Let her be yours then, France," said Lear, " for we have no such daughter, nor shall we ever see that face of hers again. Therefore begone, without our grace and blessing."

With these words Lear rose from his throne, and leaning on Burgundy's arm, left the Court.

The rest of his lords followed him, leaving France with Cordelia and her two sisters. They bade farewell to each other coldly. As soon as they were alone, Goneril and Regan began to speak of what had happened.

" You see how changeable our father is," said Goneril, " he always loved Cordelia best."

" It is his old age," replied Regan, " he has never known himself."

" At his best," Goneril said, " he has been rash, and now we must expect not only this but the peevishness of his dotage, and bad temper."

So they determined that they would plan together how best to curb their father, and to keep him from annoying them.

The Duke of Gloucester had two sons, Edgar and Edmund. Edgar was the son of his lawful wife ; but Edmund was his son by another mother. He was a cruel, ambitious young man, determined that in spite of all natural ties he would ruthlessly pursue his own advantages to the utmost. First he would oust his legitimate brother.

To this end he had forged a letter as if written by Edgar to himself. In this letter (which was signed in Edgar's name) Edgar seemed to be plotting with his half-brother to make away with their old father.

Gloucester approached, greatly distressed at the sudden happenings at Court. When Edmund saw him, he thrust the letter into his pocket, as if it were a paper which he did not wish his father to read.

" What paper were you reading ? " Gloucester asked.

" Nothing, my lord," Edmund replied.

At length, as if reluctant, he produced the folded letter, and gave it to his father to read.

Gloucester demanded how he came by it ? Who had brought it ?

" It was not brought, my lord," Edmund

answered, " that is the cunning of it. I found it thrown in at the casement of my closet."

" You know the writing to be your brother's ? " asked Gloucester.

" If the contents were good," Edmund replied, " I would swear that it was his ; but, seeing what they are, I would rather think that it was not so."

" It is his hand," said Gloucester.

" Yes, my lord," answered Edmund, " but I hope his heart is not in the contents."

" Has he never before sounded you in this business ? " Gloucester asked.

" Never, my lord," Edmund replied, " but I have often heard him declare that when sons are come to maturity, and fathers are growing old, the son should become the guardian of the father and manage his estates."

Gloucester was overcome with horror at the thought that Edgar should be plotting against him. Edmund craftily begged him to suspend his judgment until he had more certain proof, but in the meanwhile he would sound Edgar and bring him word again of what he said. So at last Gloucester left him.

When Edmund met Edgar he told him a different tale.

" When did you last see our father ? " he asked.

" Last night," said Edgar.

" Did you speak to him ? "

" Yes, for two hours."

" Did you part friendly, or did you find any sign of displeasure in him ? "

" None at all," said Edgar.

" Recollect what you may have done to offend him," Edmund went on, " and I beg you, keep out of his presence until his anger is somewhat lessened, for at this instant his rage is such that he will do you an injury."

" Some villain has done me wrong," Edgar cried.

" That is my fear too," Edmund replied smoothly. " I pray you, come with me to my lodging and thence I will bring you where you may hear our father speak. If you do stir abroad, go armed."

So Edgar, likewise deceived by his brother, hid himself apprehensively.

Lear went first to stay with Goneril. Goneril was ready to take offence, and soon found her old father's ways intolerable ; and in truth, Lear behaved as tyrannically as ever in his daughter's household. When Goneril's servants protested, he struck them. His knights were riotous, and he himself upbraided Goneril for every trifle which displeased him. Goneril therefore determined that she would check him. She told her steward, whose name was Oswald, that when Lear came back from hunting he should say that she was unwell ; and further, she commanded that he and the other servants should treat Lear with less zeal and respect, for she was determined to bring this matter to a head. Meanwhile she wrote to Regan to tell her what was happening.

Lear came back from his hunting hungry and eager for his dinner. When he entered the castle he found a strange man waiting to see him. It was Kent, though Lear did not know it. His love and loyalty for his old master was so great, that he had determined that, come what might, he would stay with him and protect him, for he knew far better than Lear the true natures of Goneril and Regan. Kent therefore disguised himself, and came to Lear asking for employment. Lear liked his blunt ways and rough speech, and agreed to employ him as his man. Then he called for his dinner and his daughter.

Oswald the steward appeared, and as Goneril had ordered, treated Lear slightingly. When Lear sent one of his knights to fetch him back, he replied that he would not come.

" My lord," said the knight, " I do not know what the matter is, but to my judgment your Highness is not treated with the same respect and affection as before."

Lear, too, had noticed it, but at first had thought nothing of it. When the steward again came into his presence, Lear called him, and began to abuse him and, when the fellow answered him back, to strike him. Before he could answer further, Kent tripped him up.

At this moment Lear's fool came in. He had seen what had happened. He took off his cox-comb cap and offered it to Kent.

" Why, my boy ? " said Lear.

" Why ? " said the fool. " For taking one's part that's out of favour. There, take my cox-comb. Why, this fellow has banished two of his daughters, and did the third a blessing against his will. If you become his servant, you must needs wear a fool's cap."

The fool was a faithful lad, but very simple, and his words, ever harping on Lear's folly, galled the old King beyond endurance.

Goneril came in full of anger that her servant had been struck.

" How now, daughter," Lear asked angrily, " why that moody face ? You frown too much these days."

" You were a pretty fellow," the fool said, " when you had no need to care for her frowning ; now you are an O without a figure ; I am better than you are now ; I am a fool, you are noth-ing."

Then Goneril spoke :

" Not only, sir, this your fool, but the rest of your insolent followers are for ever quarrelling and breaking out into intolerable riots. I had thought by telling you this that the matter would have been set right ; but now I grow fearful, seeing how you yourself have just spoken, that you approve their behaviour and allow it. If you should do so, your fault would not escape censure, nor pass unpunished."

" You know, uncle," muttered the fool, " the hedgesparrow fed the cuckoo so long that it had its head bitten off by its young."

" Are you our daughter ? " Lear asked bitterly. " What is your name, fair gentlewoman ? "

" This behaviour," Goneril answered contemptuously, " is like your other pranks. I beseech you to understand my purpose right. As you are old and reverend you should be wise. You keep here a hundred knights and squires, men so disordered and debauched that our Court is like a riotous inn. This shame calls for instant remedy. You are then desired by her, who otherwise will take what she asks, to diminish your followers ; and let the remainder be of such a kind as fit your age, and know how to behave themselves."

At this Lear broke into rage. " Darkness and devils ! Saddle my horses. Call my men together. I will not trouble you ; I have another daughter ! "

While this quarrelling was going on, Albany, Goneril's husband, joined them. He knew nothing of the cause of Lear's rage or Goneril's anger. Lear turned on Goneril and cursed her. He prayed to Nature that Goneril might never have a child, but if she did, that it should be so unnatural that she should grow old before her time, and then she would feel how bitter it was to have a thankless child.

Lear was so beside himself with rage that he began against his will to weep, and he could have torn out his very eyes for shedding tears.

" Let it be so ! " he cried, " I have another daughter who, I am sure, is kind. When she shall hear this, she will flay your wolfish face with her nails."

So calling his knights together, they mounted their horses and rode away towards Regan's castle. As soon as they had gone, Goneril sent for Oswald her steward, who at her command had written a letter to Regan, and told him to take it. Albany was much perturbed at this sudden departure of the King, but Goneril, who despised her husband for his gentle ways, would take no notice of his protests.

Lear also, as soon as he had got away from Goneril, sent a letter to Regan, which he gave to Kent, bidding him hurry and deliver it.

That night Gloucester received a message that Regan and the Duke of Cornwall intended to come to him. When Edmund learned of it he saw that here was the moment for driving his brother from his father's favour. In the darkness he called to Edgar to come out of his hiding-place. He asked him whether he had not perchance spoken against the Duke of Cornwall.

" I am sure of it," replied Edgar, " not a word."

" I hear my father coming," cried Edmund, " I will pretend to attack you. Draw your sword. Seem to defend yourself."

Then clashing his sword against Edgar's he shouted out in the darkness, as if he were fighting desperately. Edgar fled, as Edmund had warned him. As Gloucester drew near, with his servants carrying torches, Edmund made a slight cut on his own arm to make his father believe that he had been fighting desperately to save his life.

" Now, Edmund, where is the villain ? " cried Gloucester.

" Here he stood," Edmund replied, " in the dark, with his sharp sword out, mumbling wicked charms."

" But where is he ? " asked Gloucester again.

" Look, sir, I bleed," Edmund replied.

And while some went to search for Edgar, Edmund told a tale of how he had rebuked his brother for wishing to murder his father, and this, he said, had made Edgar so angry that he drew his sword and furiously attacked him, but now had fled.

" Let him fly far," Gloucester replied. " The noble Duke, my master, comes here to-night. By his authority I will proclaim that whosoever finds him shall deserve thanks, and he that conceals him, death."

By this treachery Edmund so persuaded Gloucester of Edgar's guilt that he determined to do everything to bring about his arrest. When Cornwall and Regan arrived, Gloucester told them of his sorrow.

" Was he not a companion of the riotous knights that waited upon my father ? " asked Regan.

" I do not know, madam," Gloucester replied.

But Edmund said, " Yes, madam, he was."

" It is no wonder then," Regan said ; " they have urged him to kill the old man, to spend and waste his money."

They all went in together, Cornwall and Regan greatly praising Edmund for his loyalty to his father.

Very early next morning, before it was light, Kent, who had followed Regan and Cornwall to Gloucester's castle, was stabling his horse, when Oswald, Goneril's steward, joined him. He did not at first recognize Kent as the man who had tripped him. Kent was so angry at the sight of the steward that he fell to abusing him so heartily that he was almost out of breath.

" Why," said Oswald, " what a monstrous fellow you are to rage on one that you do not know."

" What ! " cried Kent. " Do not deny that you know me ? Is it so long since I tripped up your heels and beat you before the King ? Draw your sword, you rogue ! Draw ! "

Oswald was terrified and cried out for help, whilst Kent struck him with the flat of his sword.

Oswald's cries soon brought Edmund, Cornwall, Regan, Gloucester and the servants out into the courtyard to see what was happening. Gloucester asked them what was the matter. Oswald was too breathless to speak, but Kent angrily and insolently continued to insult him ; and even when Cornwall told him to cease, he went on with his railing.

At last Cornwall asked Oswald how the quarrel had started. Oswald, who had regained his breath now that he was safe, replied that lately the King his master had struck him, and then he went on, " Being down, this man railed at me, and insulted me, which won praises from the King, and in that mood he drew his sword on me again here."

Kent in his turn spoke so insolently to Cornwall that in rage he called for his servants to bring out the stocks. Kent was locked into the stocks and left there while the others went in. He was not greatly troubled, for he was very weary, and soon fell asleep.

Meanwhile Edgar, knowing that in every place he was being proclaimed as a traitor, hid himself in a hollow tree. He disguised himself as a lunatic beggar, begrimed his face with filth, and, covered only with a blanket, wandered across the countryside crying out and screaming, " Poor Tom ! Poor Tom ! "

Next day Lear and some of his gentlemen reached Regan's castle. The first sight he saw was Kent fastened in the stocks. " Who is he," he asked indignantly, " that has set you here ? "

" It is both he and she," Kent replied, " your son-in-law and daughter."

" No ! " cried Lear.

" Yes."

" No, I say ! "

" I say yes ! " replied Kent.

" They durst not do it," said Lear, " they could not, would not do it ! Tell me at once why you deserve to be treated so ? "

" My lord," Kent answered, " when I reached your daughter and gave your letters to her, there came in a sweating messenger bringing salutations from his mistress Goneril. He delivered his letters, which they read at once. Then immediately they summoned their followers, took horses, commanded me to follow, and await their answer. When I came here I met the other messenger whose welcome had poisoned mine. He was the same fellow that was so saucy to your Highness. Like a fool, I drew my sword on him, and he raised the house with his cowardly cries. This is why your son and daughter have inflicted this shame upon me."

Lear was so moved by the insolent way that

his messenger had been treated that he could scarcely speak. His heart beat so violently that he felt it would suffocate him. He went in himself to speak with Regan. Gloucester met him with a message that they would not speak to him.

"They refuse to speak with me?" said Lear. "They are sick? Weary? They have travelled all night? These are mere excuses. Bring me a better answer."

"My dear lord," said Gloucester, "you know the fiery temper of the Duke."

"Fiery!" cried Lear. "Fiery?"

Then restraining his passion with great difficulty, he said:

"Why, Gloucester, I would speak with the Duke of Cornwall and his wife."

"My good lord," Gloucester answered, "I have informed them so."

"Informed them? Do you understand me, man?"

"Yes, my good lord."

"The King," said Lear quietly, for all his passion, "would speak with Cornwall. The dear father would speak with his daughter; commands her service. The fiery Duke, tell him that —no, not yet. Perhaps indeed he is not well; when we are out of health we are not ourselves."

But his patience was short lived, for his eye

again fell on Kent in the stocks and he began to rage.

"Why should he stay there? This action persuades me that this removal of the Duke and Regan is a plot. Release my servant. Go and tell the Duke, and his wife, that I would speak with them. Now! At once! Bid them come forth and hear me, or I will beat the drum at their chamber door!"

Gloucester went in again greatly apprehensive. At length he returned with Cornwall and Regan.

"I am glad to see your Highness," said Regan.

"Regan, I think you are," said Lear. "Beloved Regan, your sister's naught. Oh, Regan."

"I pray you, sir," she answered coldly, "be patient. I cannot think my sister should fail in her duty. If perchance she has restrained the riots of your followers, it is for some good reason."

"My curses on her!" muttered Lear.

"Sir," answered Regan, "you are old. You should be ruled by those of discretion. I pray you go back to my sister and say that you have wronged her."

"Ask her forgiveness?" cried Lear. "Go down upon my knees and say, 'Dear daughter, I confess that I am old; old men are unnecessary. I beg you on my knees to give me maintenance, bed and food.'"

"Good sir," said Regan, "no more. These are foolish pranks. Go back to my sister."

" Never ! " cried Lear. " She has cast off half my train ; looked blackly at me ; insulted me. All the vengeance of Heaven fall on her head ! " And with that he began again to curse Goneril.

" Oh, blest Gods ! " cried Regan. " You will curse me too when your rash moods are on."

" No, Regan," he said, " you will never have my curse ; your nature will never make you harsh. It is not in you to grudge my pleasures, to cut off my followers, to bandy heated words with me, and to shut me out. You know better how a child should treat its father."

While he was still speaking, the trumpet call announcing the arrival of Goneril and Albany was heard. Goneril approached. She greeted her sister warmly. Lear was aghast to see Regan take her by the hand, and rebuked her.

" How have I offended ? " sneered Goneril. " Everything is not an offence that an old man thinks so."

Then Lear's mind went back to Kent in the stocks.

" How came my man in the stocks ? " he asked.

" I sent him there, sir," answered Cornwall, " but his conduct deserved worse."

" Did you ? " Lear asked.

" I pray you, father," Regan said, " remember that you are weak. If until the end of your month you will return and stay with Goneril, dismissing half your followers, you can then come to me; for I am now away from home and have not the means to entertain you."

"Return to her," he said, "with fifty of my men dismissed? No. I would rather live in the open with the wolf and owl. Return to her? Why I could as well be brought to kneel to France and beg help of him to keep myself alive."

"At your choice, sir," said Goneril.

"I pray you, daughter," he answered quietly, for all his passion, "do not make me mad. I will not trouble you, my child. Farewell. We will meet no more. But yet," he cried, as his passion rose, "you are my flesh, my blood, my daughter, or rather a disease that is in my flesh; a boil, a plague sore. But I will not chide you. I can be patient. I can stay with Regan, I and my hundred knights."

Regan would in no way agree to this. She begged him to bring no more than five and twenty.

"I gave you all," cried Lear.

"And in good time you gave it," she answered.

Then he had a mind to go back to Goneril, for she at least would allow him fifty knights. When Goneril heard this, she said, "Hear me, my lord; why do you need twenty-five, or ten, or five, to serve you in a house where twice as many are commanded to look after you? Why do you need one?"

At this unkindness Lear's rage broke out afresh. He could endure it no longer, and crying vengeance on them all, he rushed out of the courtyard calling on his men to follow him and saddle the horses. It was now evening. The sky was overcast and the wind rising, for a storm was fast coming on.

" Let us go in," said Cornwall.

" This house is little," Regan replied, " the old man and his people cannot be housed in it."

" It is his own fault," added Goneril, " he must taste his own folly."

When all had returned into the castle, Cornwall commanded Gloucester to bar his doors.

Night came on and the storm increased as Lear wandered over the heath half mad with his rage, and alone but for the fool.

The storm grew louder and the tempest fiercer ; he began to speak to it. " Blow winds," he cried, " and crack your cheeks ! Spit fire ! Spout rain ! You are not my daughters ; I never gave you a kingdom or called you my children. I do not charge you with ingratitude, but yet I call you slavish ministers because you join with two pernicious daughters to fight against a poor old man."

Kent all this while had been trying to find his master. At last he came on him and the fool. Lear scarcely noticed him for the tumult in his mind and the storm without, which were almost unbearable. Kent at last persuaded him to seek shelter in a hovel, but Lear's wits were beginning to turn.

Meanwhile, Edmund saw a fresh chance of advancing himself still further. Gloucester, in great sorrow at the cruel treatment of the old King, spoke to him.

"I do not like this unnatural dealing," he said. "When I asked for leave that I might pity him, they would not allow me to use my own house. They charged me on pain of perpetual displeasure, neither to speak of him, plead for him, or in any way help him."

"This is most savage and unnatural," said Edmund.

"Say nothing," Gloucester replied. "There is a growing quarrel between the Dukes of Cornwall and Albany; and worse than that. I have received a letter this very night, which I have locked in my closet. There is an army already on the march which will avenge the King. We must help the King. I will search for him and secretly relieve him. Meanwhile, to hide my absence, you talk to the Duke."

When Gloucester had gone, Edmund sought his opportunity. He went to his father's closet, took the letter, and went with it instantly to Cornwall. When Cornwall heard Edmund's tale, he broke out in fury against Gloucester. "I will be revenged!" he cried, "before I leave this house."

Edmund replied smoothly, " I fear that I may be blamed for allowing my loyalty to come before my love for my father."

" I now see," said Cornwall, " that it was not altogether your brother's evil nature that made him seek his father's death."

Edmund, not wishing that the Duke's thoughts should be distracted from his father to think favourably of his brother, produced the letter which he had found, and handed it to Cornwall.

" If this paper is true, you have a mighty business in hand," said Edmund.

" True or false," Cornwall replied, " it has made you Earl of Gloucester. Find out where your father is, that he may be ready for arrest."

" If I should find him helping the King, it would confirm suspicion. I will continue to let loyalty come before affection, though it is a bitter conflict," said Edmund.

" I trust you," said Cornwall. " You will find me a dear father to you."

At length Kent found the hovel and led Lear to it. The old King was wet through and his sodden garments were blown about by the pitiless winds. His mind was wild, but even in the storm he was learning things that he had never realized before. There was born in him a feeling of pity for the poor and homeless. Lear bade the fool enter the hovel first. He had hardly gone in when he ran out again screaming with fear. Within was Edgar in his guise as the lunatic beggar. He scrambled out, following the fool and moaning, " Fathom and half, fathom and half ; poor Tom."

This was too much for Lear's feeble wits ; his mind cracked, and he became quite mad. When he saw the lunatic, naked but for his blanket, it seemed to him that he too must have had ungrateful daughters, for nothing but such ingratitude could have brought him so low. Then he began to ponder on the nature of man who must borrow from the silkworm or the sheep to clothe himself. Edgar was man himself, owing nothing to beast. A poor, bare, forked animal. With that Lear began to tear off his own clothes, until Kent prevented him. They saw some one with a torch approaching through the darkness. It was Gloucester.

He told Kent that Goneril and Regan were seeking to kill Lear. They all went back into the hovel, Lear taking the arm of the lunatic. Then Gloucester left them to find some succour.

Lear was now quite mad, and it seemed to him that he was sitting on the seat of justice trying his two daughters for dishonourably treating their father.

" Arraign her first," he cried, " it is Goneril. I here take my oath before this honourable assembly, she kicked the poor King, her father."

Edgar, for his own safety, was forced still to

play the lunatic, but at the sight of the King's
distress he almost forgot his part and began to
weep.

At length Kent persuaded Lear to lie down and
rest, but at this moment Gloucester returned.
He had overheard a plot to put Lear to death.
He had therefore brought a litter and horses. He
bade Kent lay Lear in the litter and drive him in
all haste to Dover, where he would find help. So
once more Lear was turned out into the night.
Only Edgar was left behind with the knowledge
that his miseries, however great, were slight
compared with the King's.

Meanwhile Goneril, Regan, and Cornwall were
impatiently waiting for news of Lear's arrest.
They had heard that France had landed at Dover
with an army. Goneril, with Edmund to escort
her, set out to join her husband and to raise their
soldiers.

When Gloucester returned and came into the
presence of Regan and Cornwall, they commanded in their fury that he should be bound
and tied in a chair. Regan in rage plucked him
by the beard. Gloucester protested at such
ignoble treatment.

" Come, sir," cried Cornwall, " what letters
have you had lately from France ? "

" Answer us straight," said Regan, " for we
know the truth."

" And what plot have you made," asked Cornwall, " with the traitors who have landed in the kingdom ? "

" Where have you sent the lunatic King ? " cried Regan. " Speak."

Gloucester replied, " I had a letter set down in doubtful terms which came from one who is neutral in this quarrel, not an enemy."

" Cunning," cried Cornwall.

" And false," said Regan.

" Where have you sent the King ? " asked Cornwall.

" To Dover."

" Why to Dover ? " asked Regan.

" Because," Gloucester answered boldly, " I would not see your cruel nails pluck out his poor old eyes. Nor your fierce sister stick her fangs in his anointed flesh. If wolves had howled at your gate that night, you would have let them in to shelter ; but I shall see vengeance overtake such children."

" You will never see it," said Cornwall. And with that he commanded his servants to hold Gloucester down in the chair, and then with fierce cruelty he stamped on Gloucester's eye.

" One eye will mar the other," cried the implacable Regan. " Put out the other too."

This cruelty so horrified one of his servants that he cried out to him to forbear. Cornwall was angry at this interference. He drew his sword and made for the man. The servant defended himself and gave Cornwall a mortal wound ; but Regan, snatching a sword from one of the other servants, came behind him and stabbed him in the back. Then Cornwall finished his cruel task and destroyed Gloucester's other eye.

" Where is my son Edmund ? " Gloucester cried out in his agony. " Edmund, revenge this horrid act ! "

But Regan mocked him. " You treacherous villain ! You call on him that hates you. It was Edmund who revealed your treasons to us."

Then Gloucester knew the truth that he had treated Edgar unjustly, and he prayed the Gods to forgive him for it, and to take care of his true son.

" Thrust him out of the gates," said Regan, " and let him smell his way to Dover."

So Gloucester was turned out of his castle ; but Cornwall's wound was mortal, and in a short while he was dead.

Edgar meantime was also making his way to Dover. He saw an old man coming towards him leading his blinded father. Though he must still pretend to be the lunatic, yet he now took charge of his own father and gently led him on his way.

Now that Edmund had displaced his father and had become Earl of Gloucester, his ambition grew. Goneril was falling in love with him, for long since she had tired of her mild husband, Albany. She promised to write to him.

Regan also, being now a widow, was falling in love with Edmund, and jealousy between the two sisters grew quickly. Regan found Oswald about to take a letter to Edmund from Goneril and tried to get it from him. Oswald would not give up the letter, but from his manner she knew the contents.

Edgar at last led Gloucester towards Dover. His blind father still did not recognize him, but he knew from Gloucester's words that he meant to kill himself; for Gloucester begged him to take him to the edge of the cliff and there leave him.

Edgar, however, deceived his father, pretending that he was at the cliff edge, and then, when Gloucester threw himself forward and fell stunned but unhurt on the ground, he changed his tone. He no longer whined in the voice of the lunatic beggar; instead he pretended to be a countryman. When Gloucester had revived somewhat, he was easily persuaded that his life had been saved by a miracle, and was the more willing to endure his sorrows patiently. So they went on their way towards Dover, and as they went Lear met them.

Lear was now quite mad, with flowers stuck in his hair. His talk was wild and rambling. At one time he thought himself a captain drilling recruits. Then he half recognized Gloucester, realizing that he too was the victim of an unkind child.

But help was at hand for Lear. Some of Cordelia's men met him. Lear ran away from them, but they caught him and brought him to Cordelia.

Then Oswald the steward, carrying Goneril's letter to Edmund, recognized Gloucester. There was a price on Gloucester's head and the steward thought to win it. He drew his sword, but Edgar attacked him with his staff and struck him over the head so that he fell dying. Oswald, before he died, begged him to take his letter and deliver it to Edmund. As soon as the steward was dead Edgar opened the letter ; it was, as he thought, a love-letter from Goneril to his brother. He put the letter in his pocket until there should be a fit time to reveal it to Albany.

By now Lear had at last come into the care of Cordelia. He slept, cared for by her doctor. When it was time for him to wake, he was carried by her servants into her presence, still fast asleep.

Cordelia put her arms around him and softly kissed him. He began to stir. She asked him in her gentle low voice, " How fares your Majesty ? "

Lear was dazed, and thought himself dead and waking in another world. As he opened his eyes and saw Cordelia's face before him he thought she must be a spirit in Paradise.

"You do me wrong," he murmured, "to take me out of the grave. You are a soul in bliss, but I am bound upon a wheel of fire and my tears scald like molten lead."

"Sir," said Cordelia, "do you know me?"

"You are a spirit, I know," he answered. "When did you die?" But his senses began slowly to return, and he wondered where he was.

"Look on me, sir," said Cordelia. "Hold your hand in blessing over me."

But Lear instead went down upon his knees that she might bless him. She raised him gently.

"I pray you, do not mock me," he said. "I am a very foolish, fond old man. Do not laugh at me, for as I am a man, I think this lady to be my child Cordelia."

"And so I am; I am!" she cried.

Lear looked into her face and saw her cheeks all wet with tears.

"I pray you, do not weep," he said. "If you have poison for me, I will drink it. I know you do not love me, for your sisters have done me wrong, if I remember. You have some cause; they have not."

"No cause, no cause," cried Cordelia.

"Am I in France?" he asked.

"In your own kingdom, sir," she said.

"Do not wrong me," Lear sighed.

Then the doctor advised Cordelia to take Lear in, but not to let him trouble his mind further for the present.

The armies were now gathering. Regan, with her soldiers led by Edmund, Albany and Goneril and their army came together. The leaders prepared to consult on the order of battle. Then Edgar saw his opportunity. He came up to Albany and gave him a letter.

" Before you fight the battle," he said, " open this letter. If you have the victory, let the trumpet sound to summon him that brought it ; for though I seem wretched, I can produce a champion who can prove what is declared here."

Then, without staying until Albany had read it, he made off and went back to Gloucester, his father. He led Gloucester to a tree to watch what should be the end of the battle. But not for long, for the forces of Cordelia soon yielded and fled, leaving Lear and Cordelia prisoners in the hands of Edmund. When the prisoners were brought before him, he sent them away to prison under good guard.

Lear was entirely happy to be alone with Cordelia anywhere. " Come," he said, " let's away to prison. We two alone will sing like birds in a cage, and when you ask me for my blessing, I will kneel down and ask you for forgiveness."

So they were led away.

Then Edmund called for a captain, to whom he gave an urgent command that he should go to the prison and, saying nothing to any one, put them both to death.

When Albany, Goneril, Regan, and the rest came up to Edmund, Albany praised him for his valour, and commanded that the prisoners should be used kindly.

" Sir," replied Edmund, " I have thought it fit to set the old King, and with him the Queen, under guard." But he spoke so loftily that Albany rebuked him.

" I regard you as a subordinate in this war, not as my brother," he said.

" That," answered Regan, " is as we choose. I think my will might have been asked before you spoke. He led my army and carried my commission, so he may well call himself your brother."

" Not so hot," sneered Goneril. " His own grace praises him more than any honour you can bestow."

" In my rights," retorted Regan, " he equals the best."

" He would," replied Goneril, " if he should marry you."

Then Regan cried out to Edmund, " General, take my soldiers, my prisoners, my wealth ; dispose of them and of me as you will, for I call the world to witness that I here create you my lord and master."

" Do you mean to marry him ? " asked Goneril.

" The permission is not yours to grant," said Albany to his wife. Then he went on, " Edmund, I arrest you for capital treason, and with you, this gilded serpent, my wife. As for your claim on him, Regan, my wife was first contracted to this lord, and I, her husband, will stop the banns. You are armed, Gloucester ; let the trumpet sound. If none appear to prove upon your body that you are a manifest traitor, here is my pledge. I solemnly declare, and will prove before I taste bread, that you are nothing less than what I proclaim you to be."

Regan would have answered fiercely on Edmund's part, but sickness was overcoming her. Goneril watched her grimly, for she knew the cause of Regan's sickness, and that the poison which she had given her was working well. Edmund accepted Albany's challenge.

A herald was summoned. The trumpets were sounded, and the herald made proclamation :

" If any man of quality or degree within the army will maintain that Edmund, Earl of Gloucester, is a traitor, let him appear at the third sound of the trumpet. He is ready to defend himself."

So the trumpet sounded once, twice, thrice. At the third sounding there was an answering call, and a knight fully armed, his face hidden in his helmet, appeared.

"Ask him his purpose," said Albany, "why he appears on this call of the trumpet."

"Who are you?" said the herald. "What is your name, and why do you answer this summons?"

"My name is lost," replied the knight, "yet I am as noble as the adversary I come to meet."

"Who is your adversary?" asked Albany.

"Who is he that speaks for Edmund, Earl of Gloucester?" asked the knight.

"I myself," replied Edmund. "What have you to say to me?"

"Draw your sword," replied the knight. "I here protest in spite of your strength, your youth, your honour, you are a traitor, false to your Gods, your brother, and your father; a conspirator against this illustrious Prince, and from your head to feet, a most toad-spotted traitor. If you deny it, this sword, this arm, are ready to prove upon your heart that you lie."

Edmund answered him boldly, "I might ask you your name, but since your looks and tongue show you to be of good birth, I will meet you."

Then he bade the trumpets sound, and he attacked his adversary. They fought long, but at length Edmund was forced to give ground, and fell mortally wounded.

Goneril went down on her knees beside him, greatly lamenting his fall.

"Shut your mouth, lady," Albany said, "or with this paper I will stop it."

Then he held before her face that same letter which she had sent to Edmund which so plainly revealed her guilt. Goneril snatched it from him, and would have torn it into fragments. Then she rushed away.

Edmund, knowing that his time had now come, confessed his guilt.

"What you have charged me with," he said, "I have done and more, much more. But who are you? If you are noble I forgive you."

So Edgar, for it was he, took off his helmet and revealed himself to Edmund.

"My name is Edgar," he said, "your father's son."

Albany was amazed, and asked Edgar where he had hidden himself all this while. Edgar told how he had lived as a lunatic beggar, and in this disguise had met his father newly blinded, and had been his guide, never revealing himself until just before this combat; and then he asked his father's blessing, and the poor old man, worn out with his miseries, yet rejoicing at the loyalty of his true son, had blessed him, but then died of a broken heart. Then he told of the faithfulness of Kent and of the sufferings of the old King; but the tale was broken, for one rushed in holding a bloody knife.

" Your lady, sir ! " he cried to Albany ; " your lady and her sister ! She has poisoned her ! She confessed it ! "

" I was contracted to them both," murmured Edmund grimly, " all three now marry in an instant."

Then he remembered what all this while had been forgotten, the fate of Lear and Cordelia.

" Send quickly," he said, " to the castle, for I have commanded the death of Lear and of Cordelia. The captain there had order from your wife and me to hang Cordelia, and to say that in despair she killed herself."

But before any one could speak or move, they saw Lear coming towards them, carrying Cordelia in his arms, dead. He laid her down, and looked round upon them all.

" She is gone for ever," he said, " I know when one is dead. She is dead as earth. Cordelia, stay a little. What is it you say ? " Then he bent down over her as if to listen. " Her voice was always soft and gentle and low."

So they gathered round, watching Lear as he feebly knelt beside Cordelia. The little life left in him began to flicker. Suddenly he thought that her lips moved, and with a cry of joy he fell dead over her body.

V

THE TEMPEST

THERE was once a Duke of Milan called Prospero. He was a wise man, but he cared less for state-craft than for his secret studies. He would leave the affairs of his dukedom to be managed by his brother Antonio, whilst he retired to his library and there pursued his science. Antonio was not worthy of such trust. From being his brother's deputy, he was ambitious to become the real ruler of Milan. He turned out of office those who were faithful to Prospero, and in their place he set creatures of his own. Then he plotted with Alonso, King of Naples, that if he would help him dispossess Prospero, he would henceforward pay homage and tribute.

One midnight certain men, whom Antonio had hired for the purpose, came upon Prospero at his studies. They seized him and hurried him on board a rotten little boat, and with him they placed Miranda, his daughter and only child of three years old. Nevertheless many loved the studious Duke, and especially one of the Councillors known as Gonzalo. Gonzalo made it his special care that Prospero should not be ill provided. He caused to be set on board clothes, linens, and necessaries, and, which pleased Prospero more, he added certain volumes from his library that he valued more than his dukedom.

At length the ship reached an island unknown to seamen. Prospero went ashore with Miranda, and there he built himself a cell. On this island there was only one mortal creature, a savage and deformed monster called Caliban, so brutish that he could not speak ; yet in form a man, for his mother had been a notorious witch called Sycorax. There was one other inhabitant of the island known only to Prospero, for it was a spirit of the air named Ariel. When Prospero first came to the island, Ariel was pinned and imprisoned in a cloven pine tree, where Sycorax had left him twelve years before ; but Prospero by his art released Ariel, and henceforth the spirit became his servant to do his bidding in whatever he commanded, by land or sea or air.

So Prospero and Miranda lived together on the island for twelve years, seeing no mortal creature except the brute Caliban. At last there came a day when Prospero by his art knew that those who had wronged him would shortly come into his power.

It happened that Alonso, King of Naples, had married his daughter to the King of Tunis, and with him on his ship was Sebastian his brother, and Antonio the usurping Duke of Milan. There was also Ferdinand, Alonso's young son and heir to his Kingdom of Naples, and others of his Court, and their servants, among them Trinculo his jester and Stephano his butler. As the fleet returned from Tunis a great storm arose. The ships were scattered, and Alonso's ship was carried far out of its course, until it was driven on the rocks that fringed Prospero's island. Yet this was no natural storm, for Prospero, by his art, had raised it, knowing that the time was come when he would be able to fulfill his will.

All was confusion on board the ship. As the wind carried her nearer and nearer to the rocks, the master of the ship called up the boatswain from below and bade him send the sailors aloft to take in the topsail. Alonso and the rest, alarmed by their cries and shouting, came up on deck, but the boatswain drove them down again. But all was in vain. The waves sucked the ship shorewards, until at last she was carried on to the rocks, and there stuck fast.

Miranda from the island had gazed on the wild waters and the sea mounting so high that it seemed as if it would touch the very sky. She watched the ship as it drove ashore and struck the rocks. She heard the cry of those within the vessel, and she began to weep for sorrow at their end.

Prospero bade her be comforted for no harm was done. Yet he spoke to her strangely; and, indeed, Miranda knew nothing of her father, for never yet had he told her more of himself than that his name was Prospero. The time was now come when she must learn his secret. He took off his magic gown and laid it aside. Then he bade her sit down and wipe her sad eyes; she must not grieve at the sight of the wreck, for by his art he had so ordered that not one soul had perished from the ship. Then he told her to listen carefully, for now, he said, she must know more of herself and him.

" You have often begun to tell me what I am," said Miranda, " but stopped, and answered my vain questions with ' Stay, not yet.' "

" The hour is now come," Prospero replied. " Be attentive. Can you remember a time before we came to this island ? I do not think you can, for then you were but three years old."

" Certainly, sir, I can," said Miranda.

" By what ? " asked Prospero. " By any other house ? Or person ? Or is there some image kept in your remembrance ? "

" It is far off," Miranda answered; " rather like a dream. But did I not once have four or five women that attended me ? "

" You had," said Prospero, " and more, Miranda. But how is it that this lives in your mind ? What else can you see or remember before you came here ? Or how ? "

" I remember nothing," she replied.

" Twelve years ago, Miranda," Prospero went on, " twelve years ago, your father was the Duke of Milan."

" Oh, the heavens ! " cried Miranda, " what foul play had we that we came thence ? Or was it blessed ? "

" Both, both, my girl. By foul play were we cast out, but blessedly brought hither."

So Prospero began his tale. He told her how Antonio had plotted against him with Alonso, and had set them to sea in a ship, and how at last they had reached this island, where, with Prospero as her schoolmaster, she had been brought up as carefully as few other princesses.

Miranda was sad and amazed at this strange tale. She asked her father why he had raised the storm. He replied, " By most strange accident, Fortune, once my enemy, but now my true friend, has brought my enemies to this shore, and by my art I find that on this very hour depends my future. But cease from questioning. You are inclined to sleep."

Miranda lay back and soon fell asleep, for Prospero had laid a spell upon her.

Then Prospero called for Ariel, his spirit. In a

moment Ariel was beside him, eager to do his bidding.

"Have you," said Prospero, "done what I bade you?"

"Yes, master," Ariel replied. "I boarded the King's ship. Like lightning I flickered about her, on the beak, in the waist, the deck, and in every cabin. On the topmast, the yards, the bowsprit I flamed."

"My brave spirit," said Prospero. "Was any so firm that this confusion did not drive him crazy?"

"Not one. All but the sailors plunged into the foaming sea and left the vessel. The King's son Ferdinand, his hair standing upright, was the first man to leap."

"Are they all safe?" Prospero asked.

"Not a soul perished," the spirit answered. "There is not a spot upon their garments; and as you bade me, I scattered them about this island. The King's son I landed by himself and left him, his arms folded, sitting and sighing into the air."

"How have you disposed of the sailors in the King's ship?"

"She now lies safely in harbour in the deep nook, the sailors all stowed under the hatches. And I have charmed them fast asleep. As for the rest of the fleet I scattered, they have all met again and go sadly home towards Naples, supposing that they saw the King's ship wrecked."

Prospero bade Ariel make himself like a sea nymph, but invisible to every sight. When Ariel had disappeared, he bent over Miranda and awoke her. Then he called for Caliban. Caliban came out of the cave grumbling and muttering curses upon Prospero.

" South winds blow on you and blister you all over ! " he growled.

Prospero answered him angrily, " To-night you shall have cramps. Hedgehogs shall prick you ; you shall be pinched as thick as a honeycomb."

" I must eat my dinner," Caliban grumbled. " This island's mine through Sycorax my mother, which you took from me. When you first came you stroked me and made much of me. You taught me how to name the Great and the Little Light that burn by day and night ; and then I loved you and showed you all the good things of the island, the fresh springs and the brine, the barren places and the fertile. Cursed be I that did so. All the spells of Sycorax, toads, beetles, bats, alight on you. For I am all the subjects that you have, that once was King of myself ; and here you pen me in this hard rock, while you keep the rest of my island from me."

" You lying slave ! " answered Prospero. " I used you with human care and let you sleep in my cell, until your foul behaviour became unbearable. Loathsome slave ! I pitied you, and taught you how to speak when you would gabble like a brute. I gave you words that made known your thoughts."

"You taught me language," snarled Caliban, "and my profit of it is that I know how to curse. The red plague blast you for teaching me your language!"

Prospero was greatly angered by Caliban's curses, and commanded him to fetch wood, and quickly too. Caliban shrugged his shoulders, but when Prospero threatened him with punishment, he cringed and begged for mercy. Then he shambled away to do as he was told.

Ariel was now returning, invisible to all but his master. As he came he sang. Behind him, drawn by this unseen music, followed Ferdinand the King's son.

He was amazed, for the song seemed to mourn for his father. He stood listening to the words:

> Full fathom five thy father lies;
>   Of his bones are coral made;
> Those are pearls that were his eyes:
>   Nothing of him that doth fade
> But doth suffer a sea-change
> Into something rich and strange.
> Sea-nymphs hourly ring his knell:
> Hark! now I hear them—ding-dong, bell.

Ferdinand came nearer. Prospero bade Miranda look and say what she saw.

Miranda was astonished at this sight.

" What is it ? " she said. " A spirit ? How it looks about."

" No, girl," said Prospero, " it eats and sleeps and has senses as we have. This gallant that you see was in the wreck, and though he is somewhat downcast with his grief, yet you might call him a handsome man. He has lost his friends and wanders about to find them."

" I might call him divine," Miranda answered. " I never saw anything natural so noble."

As she gazed in wonder on the young man, Prospero knew that his hopes were to be fulfilled. Miranda left his side and went closer to gaze at this new wonder. When Ferdinand saw her, he thought she must be the goddess of the island and the music hers. She spoke to him. This made him wonder more, that she should speak in his own language.

" My language ? " he cried. " I am the best of those that speak this tongue if I were only where it is spoken."

" How," asked Prospero sharply, " the best ? What if the King of Naples should hear you ? "

" I wonder to hear you speak of Naples. The King does hear me, and weeps that he does, for I myself am King of Naples ever since I saw the King my father drowned." And his eyes filled with tears at the thought that his father was dead, so that Miranda began for very pity to weep with him.

" Yes," said Ferdinand, " the King is dead and all his lords, and the Duke of Milan and his brave son too."

But Prospero pretended to be angry and spoke harshly to him, for he saw that he and Miranda had already fallen far in love, and he feared lest Ferdinand might grow to despise one who loved him so easily.

" You usurp the title that is not yours," he said sternly. " You have put yourself upon this island as a spy to win it from me, the lord of it."

" No," replied Ferdinand, " as I am a man, I did not ! "

Miranda was distressed that her father should speak so harshly. But Prospero took no notice of her pleadings.

" Follow me," he said to Ferdinand. Then to Miranda, " Do not speak for him, he is a traitor."

Ferdinand refused to obey and drew his sword, but Prospero by his magic art charmed him so that he could not move. Miranda was so full of pity that she went down on her knees and begged her father to have mercy on him, but he rebuked her.

" Silence ! " he said. " One word more and I shall chide you, if not hate you. Why do you plead for an impostor ? You think there are no more men like him ? You have only seen Caliban and me. Foolish girl, most men would think this youth as ugly as Caliban."

" I have no ambition to see a finer man,"
murmured Miranda.

Then Prospero commanded Ferdinand to follow
and obey, which he perforce did.

" Be comforted," whispered Miranda to him,
as he followed unwillingly but unable to resist.
" My father is better natured than he appears."

In another part of the island King Alonso sat
on a fallen tree, grieving heavily for his son
Ferdinand, whom he now supposed to be dead.
His lords sat by him, and old Gonzalo tried to
comfort him, but Sebastian, his brother, and
Antonio, who had usurped Prospero's dukedom,
stood apart eyeing him jealously, and mocking
Gonzalo's vain attempt to make him forget his
sorrows. But the more Gonzalo talked, the
greater Alonso's grief became. He could not
believe that by any means Ferdinand could still
be alive.

" You may thank yourself for that," said
Sebastian unkindly. " You were knelt to and
begged not to marry your daughter to an African,
and now we have lost your son for ever. The
fault is your own."

" Lord Sebastian," said Gonzalo, " though you
may speak truth, this is not the time for it."
And to distract Alonso he went on, " If I could
order this world and were the King of it, I would
make a State different from all others. I would
have no kind of trade, or magistrates ; or books ;

none should be rich or poor ; none should be
servants ; no bargaining, or boundaries ; no
tillage. None should use metal, or corn, or wine,
or oil, nor work with his hands. All men should
be idle, and women too, and everything should
grow without labour. There would be no treason,
or crime, or need of swords and knives and guns,
for Nature would bring forth all abundance to
feed my innocent people."

" God save His Majesty," mocked Sebastian.

But in a while they were so wearied with their
labours and overcome by the unseen charm of
Ariel, that one by one they began to fall asleep ;
all but Sebastian and Antonio, and they were as
wakeful as ever. When they saw the others all
lying asleep, Antonio began to whisper to
Sebastian and to hint to him.

" What might, Sebastian," he said, " what
might ? My imagination sees a crown dropping
upon your head."

" Are you awake ? " Sebastian answered.

" Do you not hear me speak ? " replied Antonio.

" I do ; but it is a sleepy language. What did
you say ? I think you must be talking in your
sleep."

Antonio saw that Sebastian was inclining to
listen to him. He went on more boldly. He
pointed at Gonzalo.

" This old lord," he said, " may try to persuade the King that his son is alive, but it is impossible that he is not drowned. Then tell me, who is the next heir of Naples ? "

" Claribel, his daughter," Sebastian replied.

" She that is Queen of Tunis ? She that now lives beyond all reach of Naples ? How can Claribel come back to Naples ? " said Antonio.

Then he paused and looked at the sleepers once more.

" Suppose," he went on, " that they were dead, not asleep. There are some that can rule Naples as well as him that sleeps. Old lords that can prate as unnecessarily as this Gonzalo. Do you understand me ? "

" I think I do," Sebastian replied.

" Are you ready to seize your good fortune ? "

" I remember," Sebastian answered, " that you supplanted your brother Prospero."

" True," said Antonio, " and see how well my garments sit on me."

" But what of your conscience ? "

" Yes, sir, where does that lie ? I do not trouble myself with conscience. Here rests your brother no better than the earth he lies upon, whom I can put to sleep for ever with three inches of my sword. And you, too, might send this old man to his everlasting sleep. As for the rest, they will say anything that we tell them."

Sebastian was at last convinced by Antonio, and was now ready to do as he asked.

" Draw your sword," he said ; " one stroke shall free you from the tribute that you pay."

" Let us draw together," Antonio replied. " When I raise my hand to strike Alonso, you kill Gonzalo."

But they had not reckoned with Ariel, who, unseen and unheard, had overlooked their plot. In a moment he was at Gonzalo's ear whispering and warning. With their swords drawn Sebastian and Antonio approached the sleeping King, but Gonzalo suddenly sat up and cried out. At this all the rest awoke and looked around.

" What is this ? " said Alonso to Sebastian and Antonio. " Why are your swords drawn ? Why do you look so ghastly ? "

Sebastian, who had his wits about him, replied smoothly, " While we stood here, guarding your rest, we heard a great bellowing like bulls, or rather lions. Did it not wake you ? "

" I heard nothing," said Alonso.

" Oh," replied Antonio, " it was a noise enough to make an earthquake."

" Did you hear this, Gonzalo ? " Alonso asked.

" I heard a strange humming, sir, which awoke me," he said. " I awoke you and shook you, and then I saw their swords drawn. Yes, certainly there was a noise. It is best we stand on our guard and leave this place."

" Lead on," said Alonso. " Let's search farther for my poor son."

So the King wandered away in his sorrow, with the others following him.

Meanwhile Caliban, wearing a long cloak which Prospero had given him to protect him from the weather, was gathering his wood. From time to time it thundered. Caliban cursed and grumbled, hating his master, but yet fearing his punishments. He saw some one approaching whose like he had never seen before. He lay down on the ground in terror, covering his head and body with the cloak and cowering beneath it.

It was Trinculo the King's jester. He too had been saved from the wreck, and was searching through the island hoping to find some shelter from the approaching storm. He saw the monster crouched on the ground. He went up to it and examined it curiously, not sure whether it was a man or a fish, or dead or alive. By the smell it should be a fish ; an ancient fish ; but yet, as he lifted up the cloak, he saw that it had legs and arms, and certainly it was not dead. But the thunder still rattled. So Trinculo, to shelter himself from the storm, crept under the cloak with Caliban until nothing showed beneath but his legs.

Then another survivor from the wreck passed by. This was Stephano, Alonso's butler. He was bolder than Trinculo, and the more so since he had found liquor. He came by singing, and as he sang he drank again and again.

Suddenly Caliban began to tremble with fright. " Do not torment me," he cried. Stephano was startled to hear a voice. He looked at the form on the earth in wonder and amazement, for it seemed to have no head, but four legs, and two of the legs were trembling.

" Do not torment me," Caliban cried again.

Stephano searched until he found Caliban's head ; and then he thrust his bottle into his jaws and gave him to drink.

From beneath the cloak came a second voice, the voice of Trinculo. " I should know that voice," he said, " it should be—but he is drowned ; and these are devils."

And he too began to tremble.

Stephano was amazed, for this monster had not only four legs but two voices. He would talk to it.

" Stephano ! " cried Trinculo from underneath the cloak.

" Mercy ! Mercy ! " said Stephano. " It is a devil, and it knows my name ! "

" I am Trinculo. Do not be frightened."

" If you are Trinculo, come out. I'll pull you out."

So he took hold of the legs that seemed likeliest to be Trinculo's, and he pulled, and dragged Trinculo out from under the cloak.

" You are Trinculo, indeed," he exclaimed, " but how came you to be part of a sea monster ? "

Trinculo was so excited to see Stephano that he pawed him all over, but Stephano told Trinculo to desist ; his stomach was too uneasy for such rough handling. Caliban sat up and watched them admiringly.

"How did you escape?" asked Stephano. "How came you hither? I escaped upon a barrel of wine which the sailors heaved overboard, and I made this bottle out of the bark of a tree with my own hands."

Caliban was eager for another taste of Stephano's bottle. He came up to him on his knees to beg for more. Stephano gave it him, and the more he drank the braver he felt himself becoming.

"I will show you every fertile inch of the island," he babbled. "I will kiss your feet. I pray you, be my god. I will show you the best springs. I will fish for you and get you wood. I will carry no more sticks for my master, but follow you, you wonderful man!"

Trinculo watched him contemptuously.

"A most ridiculous monster," he said, "to take a poor drunkard for a wonder."

But Caliban was growing more and more excited, and eager to show Stephano the wonders of the island. Stephano agreed. So Caliban led the way, with the other two following him.

By this time Prospero had set Ferdinand to work. He made him fetch logs from the wood and pile them up. Miranda was distressed to see her lover so basely employed, but Ferdinand was glad to serve her. She came out of the cave thinking that Prospero had not seen her, though all the while he was watching. She begged Ferdinand not to work so hard, but to rest himself. "For," said she, "my father is hard at study, he will not stir for these three hours. If you will sit down, I will carry your logs for you."

Ferdinand would not agree to this; so they sat down together to argue the matter out.

"You look tired," said Miranda.

"No, noble mistress," Ferdinand answered, "when you are with me, the night seems fresh as morning. I beg you, for I would mention it in my prayers, what is your name?"

"Miranda," she said, and stopped, remembering too late that her father had forbidden her to tell him her name.

"Admired Miranda!" cried Ferdinand. "I have seen many a lady, and liked many for their virtues, but all had some defect in them; but you are so perfect that you seem to be created from every creature's best."

Miranda had never heard such talk before.

"I do not know one of my sex," she answered, "I have seen no woman's face except my own in my glass. Nor have I ever seen men, except you and my father. I do not know how others look. Yet I would not wish for any companion in the world but you; nor can I imagine a shape that I should like better. But I am forgetting what my father told me."

Ferdinand answered, " I am a prince, Miranda. I believe a king, though I would not be. Hear me from my soul. The very instant I saw you my heart became your servant."

" Do you love me ? " she asked very simply.

" Beyond all else in the world," he cried, " I love you and honour you."

At these words Miranda began to weep for very joy.

" Why do you weep ? " he asked.

" At my own unworthiness," she answered. Then she looked into his face and said, " I am your wife if you will marry me ; if not, I will die your maid. You may refuse me to be your equal, but I will be your servant whether you will or no."

Ferdinand knelt before her.

" My mistress, dearest," he said.

" My husband then ? " she asked.

" With a heart as willing as prisoner ever longed for freedom."

So they took hands and promised faith to each other.

Prospero had seen it all. He went back quietly to his book, very glad that everything was turning out as he had hoped.

Stephano, Trinculo, and Caliban first made their way to the cask, where the bottle was refilled, and soon all three of them were ripe drunk. Caliban, being unused to such liquor, was the worst. He would have quarrelled with Trinculo, but he worshipped Stephano. Then Ariel came upon them. Caliban was trying to rouse Stephano against Prospero.

"As I told you," he said, "I am the subject of a tyrant, a sorcerer, who has cheated me by cunning out of my island."

"You lie!" cried Ariel.

Caliban supposed that the voice was Trinculo's and answered angrily, "You lie, you jesting monkey, you, and I wish my valiant master would destroy you. I do not lie."

"Trinculo," said Stephano severely, "if you trouble him any more in his tale, by this hand I will remove some of your teeth."

"Why," grumbled Trinculo. "I said nothing."

"Mum then, and no more."

He told Caliban to go on with his tale.

"I say he got this island by sorcery. He got it from me. If you will revenge it on him, for I know you dare, you will be lord of it and I will serve you."

"But how shall this be brought about?" asked Stephano. "Can you lead me to him?"

"Yes, yes, my lord. I will bring you to him when he is asleep, and then you may knock a nail into his head."

Ariel again cried out, "You lie. You cannot."

"You scurvy fool," said Caliban to Trinculo, thinking that it was he who had spoken, and becoming very valiant with his liquor. "I do beseech your Greatness to give him blows and take his bottle from him; when that is gone he'll drink nothing but salt water, for I'll not show him where the fresh springs are."

"Trinculo," warned Stephano, "run into no further danger. If you interrupt the monster one word more I will beat you."

"Why, what did I do?" Trinculo grumbled. "I did nothing."

"Did you not say he lied?"

And again the voice cried, "You lie."

"Do I?" said Stephano; and with that he lost his temper and struck Trinculo.

"If you like that, call me a liar again."

"I did not call you a liar," said Trinculo, rubbing his jaw. "Are you mad? This is what comes of drinking."

Caliban was very merry at the beating of Trinculo, but when Stephano commanded he went on with his tale.

"As I told you," he said, "it is his custom to sleep in the afternoon. Then you can brain him. But first take his books. Or can you batter his skull with a log, or slit his windpipe with your knife. But take his books first, for without them he is a fool like me and has no spirits to obey him, for they all hate him as I do."

Then he went on to tell Stephano of Miranda.

"I never saw a woman," he said, "except Sycorax my mother, but she surpasses Sycorax as the greatest does the least."

Stephano pondered. Then he agreed. "Monster, I will kill this man. His daughter and I will become King and Queen, and Trinculo and you shall be my viceroys. Do you like the plot?"

"Excellent," said Trinculo.

"Give me your hand. I am sorry I beat you; but while you live, keep a good tongue in your head."

"He will be asleep in half an hour," Caliban whispered. "Will you destroy him then?"

"Yes, on my honour," Stephano answered.

Caliban was so merry at this thought that he began to sing, and all the others joined in; whereupon Ariel played the tune for them, to their great astonishment. At this strange sound Stephano grew bold, but Trinculo, who was naturally a coward, went down on his knees.

"Are you afraid?" Caliban asked Stephano.

"No, not I."

"Do not be afraid," Caliban said, "this island is full of noises and sounds and sweet airs."

The sound was now going away from them, and as it went they followed it.

Meanwhile Alonso and the rest of his followers

were still wandering hopelessly through the island searching for Ferdinand. They were very weary, and at last Gonzalo could go no farther.

"By your patience, sir," he said to the King, "I must rest."

Alonso himself was tired out. They sat down; but Antonio and Sebastian drew away from the rest and whispered together.

"I am glad," said Antonio, "that he has lost all hope. Do not, because we have been prevented once, give up what we resolved to do."

"I will take the next chance," Sebastian replied.

"Let it be to-night," said Antonio. "For now they are overwearied; they will not, and cannot, be so vigilant as when they are fresh."

"I say to-night; no more," Sebastian whispered.

There was a sound of strange and solemn music. They saw coming towards them strange creatures who carried a table with food upon it. They danced about it, and gently beckoned to the King to come and eat. All stood astonished at this sight, and while they were gazing Prospero himself looked on unseen. For a while they were uncertain whether to taste or not. At length their hunger overcame them. But as they approached the table there was a crash of thunder, and Ariel, like some foul bird, descended before the table, clapped his wings, and in a moment the banquet had vanished. Then he pointed to Alonso, Sebastian, and Antonio and said sternly :

" You are three men of sin, whom Destiny has cast upon this island which men do not inhabit, for you are unfit to live amongst men, and therefore I have made you mad."

They drew their swords as if to attack him. But he went on, " You fools. I and my fellows are ministers of Fate. You may as well try to wound the winds, or stop the waters, as hurt one feather in my wing. But remember, that you three from Milan drove out good Prospero, and exposed him and his innocent child to the sea. For this foul deed the Powers, delaying, but not forgetting, have raised the seas and shores against your peace. Alonso, they have bereaved you of your son ; and I here pronounce lingering destruction, worse than any death, that shall follow you step by step, unless from the depths of your heart you repent."

With a clap of thunder Ariel was gone.

Alonso stood still, overwhelmed with his remorse, staring in front of him.

" Oh, it is monstrous, monstrous ! " he cried. " I thought that the waves told me of it ; the winds sang to me, and the thunder called out the name of Prospero ; therefore my son lies dead in the mud, and I will seek him where he lies."

He rushed away in despair. Sebastian and Antonio followed him.

" All three of them," said Gonzalo to the others, " are desperate. Their great guilt now begins to torment them. I beg you, that are more active, follow them swiftly lest they injure themselves in their madness."

Prospero had now tried Ferdinand. As soon as he saw that he did indeed love Miranda, he bade him cease from his toil, and gave his blessing to the young lovers. Then he told them to sit down, for he would show them some proofs of his skill. As they watched they heard soft music, and before them appeared the gods of old, Iris, the messenger of the gods, and Ceres, the goddess of corn and plenty, and Juno. And then there came nymphs dancing, and spirits like harvestmen. Suddenly Prospero rose, and at a word the spirits vanished away.

" I had forgotten," he said, " the foul conspiracy of the beast Caliban."

Ferdinand and Miranda were disturbed to see his sudden passion. But he comforted them, telling them not to be afraid, for those who played before them were spirits and had melted into the air, as one day towers, palaces, temples, even the whole world itself, and all living creatures would melt away without a trace ; for our lives are like a short dream in an unending sleep. He bade them leave him. So they went into the cell hand in hand together.

Then Prospero called Ariel.

" Spirit," he said, " we must prepare for Caliban. Where did you leave them ? "

" I told you, sir. They were red hot with their drinking. Then I beat my drum. At that they pricked up their ears like colts. So I charmed them, and they followed me through briars and gorse and furze, and at last I left them up to their chins in the filthy pool beyond your cell."

Prospero sent Ariel into the cave to fetch gay clothing, which they set out upon a lime tree that overshadowed the cell. Then from above they watched.

At length Caliban, Stephano, and Trinculo, wet through and filthy with mud, came tiptoeing by. Stephano had lost his bottle in the pool, and was for going back to find it, but Caliban, who knew Prospero's power too well, begged him to be quiet. Then Trinculo saw the gay clothing. He pulled down a garment, but Stephano set eyes upon it and ordered him to give it up, which he did reluctantly. Caliban grew angry and fearful, for he wished Stephano first to kill Prospero, lest he should awake and destroy them all. But the other two were so pleased with the clothes that they took no notice of Caliban except to lay the clothes upon him and tell him to carry them off. They were still intent on their loot when certain of Prospero's spirits, in the shape of hounds, appeared and sprang upon them, barking fiercely, so that they ran away howling with terror.

All things were now ready for Prospero's plans to be brought to an end. The master and the sailors awoke from their deep sleep, and there saw to their wonder that their ship was unharmed and riding at anchor in a still bay. They looked about them, and then went ashore to find the King.

Prospero made his way to the rock that stood above his cell, and there, with arms outstretched, he bade farewell to the spirits that had been his servants, for from henceforward he would no longer use his tragic art any more.

The spell was now dissolving. Alonso, still dazed and frantic, drew near, and beside him went Gonzalo. Sebastian and Antonio followed. Unknowing, they entered the magic circle which Prospero had made and there stood charmed. Prospero went up to them, but they did not know him. First he spoke to Gonzalo, welcoming him as his preserver. Then he spoke to Antonio, but as yet his senses were numbed with the charm. Even the others did not recognize him.

So Prospero sent Ariel into the cave to bring him his robes as Duke of Milan. He laid aside his magic garment and stood before them in his royal cloak. Then he spoke to Alonso. " Behold," he said, " behold the wronged Duke of

Milan, Prospero. That you may know that I am a living man, I embrace you and I bid a hearty welcome to you and all your company."

Alonso was so overcome by the strange things that he had suffered, and by his penitence, that he answered, " If you are indeed Prospero, I give you back your dukedom, and do pray you forgive me for the wrongs I have done to you. But how can Prospero be living and be here ? "

Then Prospero took Gonzalo by the hand and welcomed him too. But to Antonio he said, " You most wicked man, I will not soil my mouth by calling you brother. Yet I forgive you too, though I will take my dukedom back from you."

" If you are Prospero," said Alonso, " tell us how you were saved. How have you met us here who three hours ago were wrecked upon this island, where I have lost my dear son Ferdinand ? "

" I am sorry for it," said Prospero.

" It is an irreparable loss," Alonso answered.

" I too," said Prospero, " have had a like loss."

" You a like loss ? "

" As great a matter as yours, and as fresh. I have lost my daughter."

" A daughter," cried Alonso, " oh, heavens ! If only they were living in Naples King and Queen there. When did you lose your daughter ? "

" In this last tempest," Prospero replied. But he would not tell them more except to say again that he was indeed Prospero, who had been thrust out of Milan, and thence most strangely was cast upon this very island where they were wrecked. He bade them welcome to his cell. Then he went to the entrance of the cave and drew aside the curtain that was before it. There sat Ferdinand and Miranda playing chess, but so busy with gazing at each other that they saw nothing else.

Alonso ran forward eagerly to embrace his son. When Ferdinand saw him, with a cry of joy he knelt before his father. Miranda, looking upon Alonso and all the others, was amazed.

" How many goodly creatures are there here ! " she cried. " How beauteous mankind is ! Oh, brave new world that has such people in it ! "

But Prospero answered sadly, " It is new to you."

" Who is this maid ? " asked Alonso. " Is she the goddess that parted us and brought us together ? "

" Sir, she is mortal," said Ferdinand. " She is the daughter of this famous Duke of Milan, of whom I have so often heard but never saw before. I have chosen her, for I could not ask my father for his advice, nor did I think I had a father."

So Alonso's troubles ended in great joy as he gave them his blessing.

The time of Ariel's release was now near, but there were still a few tasks for him to perform. First he brought to them the master of the ship and the boatswain. Then Ariel flitted away, to come back driving before him Stephano, Trinculo, and Caliban, now very sorry for themselves. Prospero told them to go in and prepare his cell.

Then he invited Alonso and the rest to stay with him that night, when he would tell them the story of his life.

"And in the morning," said he, "I will bring you to your ship and so to Naples, where I hope to see the marriage of these two, our dear beloved, and then I will go back to my Milan."

"I long to hear the story of your life," said Alonso.

"I will tell you all," Prospero answered, "and then I promise you calm seas and winds for our journey homewards."

Then for the last time he called Ariel. And as the others entered the cave he said, "Ariel, this is your duty ; then be free, and farewell."

THE END

PRINTED IN GREAT BRITAIN AT
THE PRESS OF THE PUBLISHERS